Social work and HIV/AIDS

Riva Miller & Derval Murray

VENTURE PRESS

Published by
VENTURE PRESS
16 Kent Street
Birmingham
B5 6RD

British Library Cataloguing-in-Publication Data
A catalogue record for this book is available from the British Library

ISBN 1 86178 029 X (paperback)

Design, layout and production by
Hucksters Advertising & Publishing Consultants,
Riseden, Tidebrook, Wadhurst, East Sussex TN5 6PA

Cover design by:
Western Arts
194 Goswell Road
London
EC1V 7DT

Printed and bound in Great Britain by
Biddles Ltd, Guildford and King's Lynn.

Contents

Acknowledgements ii

Preface iii

Background to HIV and social work 1

HIV infection in the 1990s 15

Dilemmas and practice issues 29

Counselling interventions for social workers in HIV 43

Interventions through the stages of HIV infection 57

Case examples: social work issues 71

Epilogue 89

References 93

Appendix: abbreviations 95

Acknowledgements

We firstly want to attribute the idea for this book to Laura Middleton and to thank her for her encouragement and helpful editorial comments to early drafts. The Public Health Laboratory Service, Colindale kindly supplied the graphs and tables. Our colleagues in the AIDS Counselling, Social Care and Prevention Unit have shown exemplary practice which helped us formulate and confirm our ideas. Social work colleagues in many London and out-of-London boroughs have contributed to this book by mere contact with us. We especially thank Mark Thrailkill for so painstakingly editing our script and Simone Kaptur for designing the graphics. Finally, our grateful thanks go to individuals and their families who have taught us so much.

Riva Miller and Derval Murray

Preface

Social work's role in the prevention and management of the AIDS pandemic has never been in doubt. The profession's unique blend of therapeutic ability, its experience as an advocate for the marginalised in society, and its practical use of community resources places social work in a position to contribute to the care of those affected and infected by HIV.

The question may arise, however, at different times and in different geographical areas as to whether that role should be a specialist or generalist one. This distinction currently differs from country to country. In the United Kingdom it differs from region to region within the country. There are some social workers who appropriately fill specialist posts, but in many settings HIV has a lower priority amongst other commitments. In my view, social workers in all settings have a professional responsibility to respond with the relevant mix of knowledge, skill, and self-awareness to people affected or infected by human immunodeficiency virus, or at risk of becoming so.

The virus also presents a dilemma to social work educators. As early as 1988, Harvey Gonchros, a noted American social work educator, is quoted as saying "to understand AIDS is to understand social work". Social workers need accurate, up-to-date information and sufficient self-awareness in relation to sex and sexuality to use their therapeutic skills competently when dealing with issues surrounding HIV infection. The short professional education and training period is already overloaded with a plethora of other concerns. This has resulted on the part of some social workers in a knowledge gap and the consequent reluctance to involve themselves with these neglected issues in practice.

Both as practitioner and educator, I welcome this book as an important contribution to the literature on social work and HIV. It takes a generalist's stance, outlining what social workers need to know about, communicate sensitively about, and advocate for effectively.

Riva Miller and Derval Murray are long-standing social work practitioners with extensive managerial and educational experience and expertise. Their professional backgrounds, substantially in medical settings, place them well to provide the necessary amount of background knowledge and information to other social workers interested in functioning in this area or who come across HIV issues in their daily practice. The interventions that they discuss stem directly from practice. Above all, their sensitive self-awareness to the people with whom they work is manifest in the case examples of their practice. I will use this book as a teaching resource, and believe that social workers, no matter in what setting they operate, will find it a valuable reference and guide book to an important field of social work practice.

Jill Stevens, Dipl Soc Sc, M Litt, AMIA
Lecturer, Department of Social Policy and Social Work,
University College of Dublin.
Senior Supervisor,
Marriage and Relationship Counselling Service,
Dublin.

REFERENCES

Canadian Association of Schools of Social Work (1988). *AIDS and Social Work Training in Canada.*

Foreman M & Mulcahy F (1997). "Social Work, HIV and Irish Women" in *Irish Journal of Social Work Research*: 1:1; 68-77.

Background to HIV and social work

INTRODUCTION

This book reviews the place, dilemmas, and tasks of social work in relation to Human Immunodeficiency Virus (HIV) infection through the last two decades. It suggests guidelines for integrating HIV treatment and care into day-to-day social work practice.

The story of the natural history of HIV infection to date has been characterised by alternating periods of new, promising developments followed by reversals in hopes and expectations. To some extent this is due to the rapid introduction of new treatments, often before the efficacy or long term consequences have been fully assessed. One consequence of new monitoring tests and emerging treatments is that people are living longer but developing other complicated illnesses affecting day-to-day living and prognosis. This "STOP GO" picture of new treatments, increased survival, the appearance of other complicated illnesses, and emerging drug reactions, has led to periods of optimism followed by pessimism for patients and their families and health care workers alike. It is against this background that the social work role and tasks shall be considered.

Social work can make a unique contribution to all aspects of HIV management because of its long tradition in medical settings dealing with the impact and implications of illness on individuals and those connected with them. Increased knowledge about the natural history of HIV infection, advances in treatment and management of HIV disease, as well as the many changes in the statutory and voluntary sectors have affected the task and role of social work in this particular field. Special aspects of HIV management for social workers in relation to medical treatment, changes in the relevant legislation, and subsequent re-organisation of social service delivery will be highlighted against the background of the emergence and course of the epidemic to date.

Throughout this book the authors alternate between the words "patient" and "client". These terms are agency related. For those with an HIV diagnosis and attending hospital the word "patient" is used; the term "client" refers to those attending local authority social services departments. This book is intended to complement the comprehensive HIV and social work book (Gaitley, et al.; 1993) which goes into greater detail about legislation and different aspects of social work and HIV. Used together, these two books attempt to place HIV and social work on a firm and formal basis. A community perspective is addressed by other authors which dovetails with this text (Singh & Madge, 1998). The medical information in relation to the treatment and management of HIV may change in the light of new knowledge. Nevertheless, the basic principles described can be adapted to deal with emerging issues in HIV.

Emergence of a disease

In the United States in 1981 Acquired Immune Deficiency Syndrome (AIDS) was first recognised as being a new, unusual, and fatal disease. It primarily affected homosexual men who presented acutely unwell with rare forms of pneumonia (Pneumocystis Carinii Pneumonia (PCP)) and cancer (Kaposi's Sarcoma (KS)). These cases were investigated by the Centre for Disease Control (CDC) in Atlanta, USA. It became clear that the underlying cause of these infections and cancers was an infectious agent transmitted through unprotected sexual contact. Later, it emerged that intravenous-drug users and people with haemophilia were also developing diseases associated with immune deficiency. The underlying pathogen was a blood-borne virus. It took some time for the various pieces of the puzzle to be put together. The virus which caused the immune deficiency (which led to AIDS) was identified in 1983-4 and first named HTLV 111; later it was renamed Human Immunodeficiency Virus (HIV).

An antibody test for the detection of the presence of antibodies to HIV became available in 1985. This enabled HIV antibody testing to be offered to people who believed they were infected or who were worried that they might have been at risk of infection. This test was initially available in sexually transmitted diseases (STD) clinics, hospitals (where individuals presented as unwell), and later in *ad hoc* anonymous testing sites. In the UK, HIV antibody testing was originally carried out in genito-urinary medicine (GUM) clinics attached to hospitals, in hospital wards and out-patient clinics, some private clinics, and later in separate HIV testing clinics, usually attached to hospitals. (Squire, et al.; 1991

POPULATION PATTERNS

THE EARLY YEARS.

AIDS first presented in large cities (New York, San Francisco, Los Angeles, Sydney, London) which attracted people wishing to pursue different or alternative lifestyles and similar interests. Large cities enabled people to preserve some anonymity, especially amongst homosexual and bisexual men.

In the early days of the epidemic, the lack of drug treatment for HIV infection meant that many homosexual men were reluctant to consider having an HIV antibody test, even if they were worried about having been at risk of infection. In those days there seemed to be little advantage for people to know that they were infected, apart from using this knowledge to practise "safer sex" and waiting for symptoms to present. Many decided against testing because of concerns about discrimination and stigma if their status should become known. Over the years, more has become known about the natural history of HIV infection, and major advances have been made in prevention and treatment of HIV-related illnesses. This has led to significant change in views about testing. Believing that they may have been at risk of infection many homosexual and bisexual men have come forward for testing in order to optimise treatment possibilities for themselves. This population, since the beginning of the epidemic, has kept itself well informed of advances in treatment and has disseminated this information through the gay community and beyond.

Early in the epidemic intravenous-drugs users were

found to be infected with HIV through sharing of drug-using equipment and sexual contact. This group of people, who can be hidden and marginalised in society, often have limited contact with health care professionals and social workers. In the UK (excluding Scotland), the spread of HIV infection through the drug-using population seems to have been relatively low. This is in contrast to other places in the world such as the US and other European countries (including Ireland, Scotland, Italy, Spain, and France) which have a high incidence of HIV infection amongst drugs users.

People with haemophilia were found to be infected with HIV early in the epidemic, through treatment with Factor VIII and IX concentrates made from human plasma. Their sexual partners, in some cases, were also infected. Consequently some children were infected through vertical transmission (infected mother to infant). People with haemophilia and their families receive their medical and psychosocial care for both haemophilia and HIV from specialised hospital units.

A small number of people who received blood transfusions in the early 1980s in the UK were infected with HIV and discovered this through the development of illness or through the tracing of infected donors via the Blood Transfusion Service.

As the epidemic progressed it became apparent that people, other than those perceived to be in the "high risks" groups, were also being infected (heterosexual men and women). Some of these people, not perceiving themselves to be at risk of infection, often presented late, after symptoms appeared, and had advanced HIV disease.

As time passed it became apparent that some infants and children were infected with HIV through vertical transmission from mother to child during pregnancy, delivery, or in the postnatal period through breast milk. In some cases a diagnosis of HIV in an unwell child is the first indication of HIV infection in a family.

The epidemic in the US has now moved into vulnerable, disadvantaged communities, particularly in the major cities. Higher numbers of black Afro-Caribbean men, women, and children have been found to be infected through drug use, sexual contact and vertical transmission. In the UK a similar pattern is emerging with many men, women, and children, particularly from sub-Saharan Africa (visitors, students, or asylum seekers) presenting with HIV infection. Other vulnerable or disadvantaged people are emerging in our society either at high risk of infection or already infected (people with learning disabilities, psychiatric illness, young men and women in care or leaving care, and prisoners). HIV infection is complicated by poverty, single parenthood, inadequate housing and access to specialist medical care.

In central London the population with HIV is composed of mainly:

- Gay and bisexual men infected with HIV;
- Asylum-seeking men, women, and children (mainly from sub-Saharan Africa);
- Heterosexual men and women infected via sexual contact;
- People with haemophilia and their sexual contacts;
- Some drug users (infected via shared needles and syringes);
- Infants and children infected through vertical transmission.

In other parts of the UK and Ireland drug users infected with HIV and their families are the major focus of social work experience in the field of HIV. Work with this group is comprehensively dealt with by Mounteney and Shapiro in *Drugs, Children and Families* (1998).

Social Implications.

From the early years individuals with HIV, their contacts and families experienced a wide range of psychological and relationship difficulties (Carballo & Miller, 1989), including fears and concerns about:

- Disclosure of status that might result in discrimination;
- Whom to tell and how to tell others;
- Loss of income and poverty;
- The impact on their families;
- How to manage the future from a practical point of view;
- Who will care for them if they become ill.

A combination of factors contributed to these fears and concerns including:

- The nature and uncertain course of HIV infection;
- Routes of transmission;
- Fear of contamination and infection;
- The focus on people leading different lifestyles;
- Stigma and discrimination.

The stigma associated with HIV infection, especially in the early years, made those infected, their partners and families, reluctant to engage with the usual community services. They were particularly afraid that news of their infection would become known in their communities. There are instances of people infected with HIV having suffered discrimination in the work-place, nurseries and schools, social groups, and health care settings.

As time has passed, the general population has become more educated about HIV infection, leading to a reduction in some overt aspects of discrimination. Many companies and institutions have developed policies to deal with HIV infection. Likewise professional bodies, such as the British Medical Association and the Royal College of Nursing, have developed guidelines for the management of members found to be infected with HIV.

Despite these moves, the fear of stigma and discrimination remains and patients continue to be reluctant to use services which could provide them with additional support and assistance. Many people from ethnic minority communities, as well as those whose immigration or residential status in the UK is uncertain, are reluctant to come forward for testing and treatment due to fears that they will be deported if their infection becomes known to the relevant authorities.

Social workers with their strong commitment to and experience in advocacy with disadvantaged groups have a particularly important role to play in helping these individuals access HIV testing, treatment, support, and care.

Disease Patterns

Early Years

In the early 1980s, with little or no treatment available for AIDS-related conditions, survival following one serious opportunistic infection was rare and individuals usually died within a short space of time (usually in the order of six months).

Middle Years

During the late 1980s and early 1990s more became known about the diagnosis, treatment, and prevention of some opportunistic infections, and survival time following an AIDS diagnosis improved. This, combined with the development of new antiretroviral treatments, meant that people with an AIDS diagnosis were living longer (in the order of three years). Nevertheless, people experienced disabilities in different ways and some required care at home.

In 1985, when zidovudine (AZT) first became available, there was great optimism that this would lead to HIV becoming a more manageable illness. However, around 1992, as drug resistance developed and side-effects to the drug were recognised, some patients became wary about taking this medication. Early optimism was followed by years when there appeared to be no major breakthrough on the horizon. Patients and doctors alike became more despondent about the epidemic.

Late 1990s

Then in 1997 there was a further surge of optimism with the advent of combinations of antiretroviral drugs which appear to be more effective in halting the progression of disease (see next chapter on *HIV infection in the 1990s*). Some patients who have benefited from these new treatments are having to re-evaluate their future plans with some considering a return to work. However, there still remains much uncertainty about the long term efficacy of these new treatments which poses different dilemmas for patients and doctors alike.

Management of HIV Infection

Early Years

In the early days of the epidemic, AIDS was seen primarily as a new and puzzling disease mainly involving medical specialists from GUM clinics, infectious diseases units, virology, and immunology. These doctors, faced with individuals having an aggressive, terminal disease for which there was little treatment, no cure, and widespread psychosocial implications, turned to other health care professionals for assistance in managing the distress and many uncertainties that these patients were experiencing.

In the UK, these patients were primarily seen by health advisers in GUM clinics and by psychologists whose expertise was sought in managing the anxiety, depression, and other difficulties experienced by patients. Those patients who feared disclosure of their status to others attended GUM clinics where confidentiality rules were already in existence through the Venereal Diseases Regulations of 1974. Specialist HIV units also were guided by this additional confidentiality as a way of encouraging those at risk to come forward for testing and treatment.

Thus expertise in diagnosing and managing HIV-related conditions became located mainly in GUM clinics of large teaching hospitals where patients felt more comfortable in disclosing issues about lifestyle and sexual orientation. Fear of stigma continued to deter patients, partners, and families from involving other services (district nurses, social workers, home helps), and few disclosed their status to their general practitioners (GPs). These patients were largely cared for in hospital or at home by family members, partners, and friends and were supported by emerging voluntary organisations.

Gay communities in the big cities developed specialist volunteer organisations to provide practical assistance and emotional support for people infected and affected by HIV (e.g. Shanti Project in San Francisco, Gay Mens Health Crisis in New York, Ankali Project in Sydney, the Terence Higgins Trust in the UK). In the early years of the epidemic excellent care for gay men and their contacts provided by such voluntary organisations reduced the necessity for the involvement of statutory community health and welfare services. Haemophilia societies likewise collected information and developed specialist services to support these patients and families.

This combination of factors led to the management of HIV being confined to a small group of medical and other health care professionals working primarily in the field of HIV. Prior to HIV testing, counselling was recommended to address some of the psychological and social implications of HIV. This counselling was mainly provided by health advisers and specialist psychologists in GUM clinics and hospitals. This exclusive management encouraged a veil of secrecy and mystique to develop around the whole area of HIV infection.

HIV AND SOCIAL WORKERS

EARLY YEARS

The particular medical specialities dealing with HIV did not traditionally have much, if any, contact with the social work profession, nor did those individuals first affected by the disease (homosexual and bisexual men), who were on the whole a hidden population of young, healthy people. Their main contact with health services was with GUM clinics for diagnosis and treatment of STDs (syphilis and gonorrhoea). Health advisers were usually involved in relation to contact tracing or partner notification.

Some IV drugs users, on the other hand, were involved with the social workers because of child protection issues or as a result of a transgression of the law. Some alcohol and drug agencies took up the challenge of HIV by providing needle-exchange programmes which helped to disseminate knowledge about HIV and thus reduce the transmission of HIV between users On the whole social workers did not become actively involved with people with HIV for some years due to the:

- Specialist developments for the management of HIV which precluded the majority of health care professionals from becoming aware of the presence of HIV in their work environment, and of the implications of HIV for individuals and families;

- Low profile of HIV in day-to-day social work practice, due to the lack of specialist knowledge, little first-hand experience, and fear of the disease;
- Perception of social work managers from an organisational point of view, that GUM services with specialist staff had the expertise and resources to deal with people with HIV and AIDS;
- Protective attitude of some specialists in the field of AIDS towards their patients and an unwillingness to involve social workers, district nurses, and GPs in patients' care. This was in part patient-led due to fears of breaches of confidentiality and resulting discrimination.

A few social workers encountered the problem early through working with patients with haemophilia and in special clinics in health settings (Bor *et al*, 1987, Miller *et al*, 1987).

On the whole the social worker's role was given less prominence than that of psychologists who were enlisted to deal with the overwhelming psychological, emotional, and social sequelae (Miller *et al*, 1986). This heightened the special aspects of HIV and led many social workers to believe that they did not have the knowledge or skills to deal with such complex issues.

Despite their extensive experience in dealing with chronic illness, stigmatised groups and difficult issues in fields as diverse as child care, mental health, learning disabilities, and ethnic minorities social workers were reluctant to come forward. This was reinforced by the myth that AIDS could only be dealt with by professionals with specialist knowledge and training in AIDS counselling and an ability to work sensitively with people of different lifestyles and sexual orientation. Special courses and organisations were established (NACTU), reinforcing the view that the management of HIV was very different from other serious and life–threatening illnesses.

National and International Social Work Developments

Early Years

- 1985: The British Association of Social Workers "Special Interest Group on HIV" began working on a briefing document on HIV for members of the profession. This was initiated by the Health and Handicap Advisory Panel of BASW in response to a DHSS press release entitled "NHS to Develop AIDS Counselling Services";
- 1985: Scottish Guidelines on AIDS for Social Work Personnel;
- 1986: "AIDS: Briefing for Social Workers"
  Specialist social work posts in some local authority settings were created;
- 1988: The International Federation of Social Workers and the International Federation of Schools of Social Work, in collaboration with the World Health Organisation's Global Programme on AIDs, began to examine the profession's role, special contribution and involvement;
- 1989 the US National Association of Social Work spearheaded the first International Conference on Social Work and HIV held in Boston, USA.

Middle Years

During these years, specialist HIV clinics and hospital wards became busier with increasing patient numbers. Careful discharge planning from hospital became imperative to enable patients' safe return home and to maximise their options in how they wished to live their lives. Hospital staff alone could not meet these needs. Alongside this, community services were becoming aware of the myriad issues and complex needs people with HIV and their contacts were experiencing in maintaining themselves at home (ranging from 24-hour care to practical assistance to enable people to continue to work).

Social workers, especially in the larger urban centres, carried out needs assessments and organised tailor-made home-care arrangements. Most of these patients, being young, single, and living away from home, did not have the resources of family to assist with their care. Often this was from choice because they did not want to reveal their illness to parents who might not be sympathetic to their lifestyle. Many did not want to return to their families who lived outside large urban areas because they wanted the specialist medical care available at large teaching hospitals. These factors often meant that considerable home care (provided mainly by social services) was required to enable such patients to manage out of hospital.

Thus, social workers became drawn into work with people with HIV through discharge planning, accessing benefits, housing, and arranging home care. Many realised that their existing skills were very adequate to deal with such problems.

Later Years

In later years as more treatments became available, people with HIV and AIDS were living longer. Problems such as access to specialist public housing, social security benefits, and home care became pressing issues and patients were referred to, or referred themselves, to local authorities' social services for assistance. Some social workers, feeling the lack of specialist knowledge and skills, tended to see themselves only as housing and benefits accessors and avoided becoming more actively involved in a wider range of work with these patients.

As the nature of the epidemic changed, it involved more family work, particularly with young children and people who are poor, disadvantaged, and those with mental health problems and learning disabilities. In these situations, HIV complicates an already existing difficulty. These are groups of people with whom social workers traditionally have a great deal of experience.

Late 1990s

As it became obvious that women (and in some cases whole families) were infected with HIV, social workers have become more involved in helping provide innovative and flexible care, support and counselling. In the early days discussion in social services focused on whether children being received into care or placed for fostering or adoption should be tested for HIV. Who should be told the diagnosis was a matter of much debate in these situations, especially where a parent or child was infected or at risk of infection. Local authority departments developed policy documents around these issues.

In more recent times the focus has switched to the particular needs of children (affected by or infected with HIV) and their families. Under the Community Care Act 1990 complex care packages are developed to support the family unit by providing practical help including assistance with:

- Bringing children to and from nurseries or school;
- Accessing child minders or nursery places;
- Arranging domestic chores to relieve parents who are unwell;
- Transport to and from hospital appointments;
- Arranging respite care for individuals or families.

For children infected with HIV, complex care arrangements need to be made to meet the needs of both parents and children who are unwell and who require specialist medical care and practical assistance in the home.

Alongside developments in the statutory services various voluntary agencies developed social work initiatives for children in relation to HIV:

- Barnardo's specialist service "Positive Options", with a brief to help HIV-infected parents plan for the future care of their children;
- Positively Women, a self-help organisation for women with HIV, employed a specialist social worker to work with infected women to help them plan for the future care of their children;
- Grandma's was established in the London area to provide volunteer child care in the home.

CHANGES IN SOCIAL SERVICES PROVISION

The 1990 NHS and Community Care Act had an impact on how social services departments provided services. Prior to this Act, social services departments had some autonomy in choosing how they provided services. Since the introduction of the 1990 Act, social workers have become care managers and their role and involvement with clients is much more circumscribed. The focus is now on actual need at the time of presentation rather than on taking a more proactive approach in order to pre-empt problems in the future. The development, management, and review of care plans is carried out by the care manager, but the services are very often provided by other agencies. Thus much of the work traditionally done by social workers is now referred out to other agencies with the care manager acting as a purchaser of "packages of care" for the service user. There appears to be little scope for social workers to be involved in HIV-prevention work, casework, or proactive planning for future problems.

Conclusions

More social work focus and involvement are still required to help parents make plans for the care of children in the event of their hospitalisation or death. Social services children and family teams need to link with parents before a crisis occurs. There is a need to continue to work with children whose parents have died to help them deal with their loss and in some cases their own illness.

This book reviews some of the particular dilemmas surrounding HIV and suggests some guidelines for social work practice. The ideas and skills described can equally be applied to other illnesses and difficult situations.

We are in a new and exciting phase in the expansion of knowledge about the natural history of HIV infection and in the development of more effective antiretroviral treatments to combat the HIV virus. It is vital that social work practice is developed and adapted in the light of new and emerging knowledge and treatment. We believe that the basic principles as described here will remain the same even though the nature of HIV infection may be more chronic than acute.

HIV infection in the 1990s

INTRODUCTION

Social workers require a background knowledge and some understanding of the diagnosis, monitoring, treatment, and prognosis of HIV infection to:

i Work effectively with individuals and their families;
ii Plan appropriate packages of care;
iii Liaise appropriately with health care teams.

HIV infection is a complex medical condition, manifesting itself in different ways as it can affect many different systems in the body. In the early stages of infection symptoms are not usually apparent. As the infection progresses, the immune system becomes depleted and clinical symptoms appear (chronic fatigue, persistent oral/vaginal thrush, diarrhoea, skin rashes, night sweats). In the more advanced stages, there can be visual and co-ordination problems (caused by other infections such as CMV), eating difficulties (caused by oral candida, nausea, vomiting), extreme loss of weight and fatigue. The manifestations of HIV disease affect people differently; some develop symptoms quite early on following infection, others do not know that they are infected until they become acutely ill. Symptoms can fluctuate over time with people having periods when they feel well and times when they are unwell.

Women can develop gynaecological problems (chronic vaginal infections, pelvic inflammatory disease (PID)) and these might be the first indication of infection. Children may present with different manifestations of HIV disease (failure to thrive, unexpected fever, diarrhoea, chronic pulmonary symptoms, skin problems). Some of them become seriously ill in the first year of life, whilst others may not show any symptoms until they are several years of age.

All these factors contribute to practical, social, and psychological implications for day-to-day living and relationships.

HIV infection is defined as:

- Asymptomatic (no overt clinical symptoms);
- Symptomatic (minor symptoms, which do no not generally interfere with day-to-day living, to those of a more-serious, persistent nature;
- Advanced HIV infection. A diagnosis of AIDS is made when patients develop certain types of tumours (Kaposi's sarcoma) or opportunistic infections (a group of illnesses – pneumocystis carinii pneumonia (PCP), tumours, TB, specific diarrhoea) which, in people with intact immune systems, only cause minor illness but in those with poor immune function cause different and more-severe illness. Women are classified as having AIDS if they develop cervical cancer. In children, failure to thrive (loss of weight and height), or lymphocytic interstitial pneumonitis (LIP – a combination of symptoms of the respiratory system), constitutes an AIDS diagnosis.

HISTORICAL BACKGROUND TO DIAGNOSIS, TREATMENT AND CARE

In the mid-1980s it was estimated that over time one in 10 HIV-infected people would develop AIDS. Some years later it became apparent that the majority of infected people would develop AIDS. In the late 1990s, treatments introduced earlier and at critical times delay progression to AIDS. Survival following an AIDS diagnosis has improved from less than one year in 1985 to several years in the1990s. Now in the late 1990s survival may be extended with the use of combinations of antiretroviral drugs.

Lack of certainty or consistent answers to some questions about prognosis, treatment, and risk behaviour (oral sex) have persisted. Nevertheless advances in research, over time, have brought more clarity in a number of areas, including:

- Routes of transmission;
- Reliability and specificity of antibody tests;
- Monitoring of disease progression treatments (CD4 counts, viral load);
- Efficacy of antiretroviral and other prophylactic treatments.

In the 16 years since AIDS was first recognised as a new clinical entity, it has been the subject of intense medical, scientific, and psychosocial investigation and research. During this time physicians have moved from recognising a particular constellation of opportunistic infections and malignancies that constitute an AIDS diagnosis to an understanding that this is the end result of a progressive, relentless destruction of the human immune system caused by infection with HIV. In recent years a greater number of medical interventions have changed the focus from crisis management of acute illness to:

- Clinical and laboratory monitoring of those found to be infected;
- The early introduction of antiretroviral treatments to reduce viral replication, increasing immune function and slow disease progression (BHIVA, 1997);
- Prophylactic regimes to prevent the development of opportunistic infections (pneumocystis carinii pneumonia, tuberculosis).

Despite these advances, patients and their clinicians are still faced with difficult treatment choices. There remains an absence of complete information about when to introduce combination therapy, which drug therapies are most efficacious, side-effects of these treatments, and their impact on long term survival. It is against this background that the social work approach to practice and development of care packages for those with HIV infection must be considered.

EPIDEMIOLOGY

The World Health Organization UNAIDS in November 1996 reported:

Worldwide figures

- 29.4 million HIV infections;
- 15.5 male;
- 11.3 female;
- 2.6 children.

In 1996 3.1 million new infections occurred

- The majority of these infections occurred in Third World and in people under the age of 25;
- 75-85% of all infections were transmitted heterosexually;
- 63% of the total HIV epidemic is in Africa;
- There are emerging epidemics in India, Far East, Eastern Europe.

Estimated number of HIV-infected people alive: mid-1996 by region (percentage of total of 21.8m)

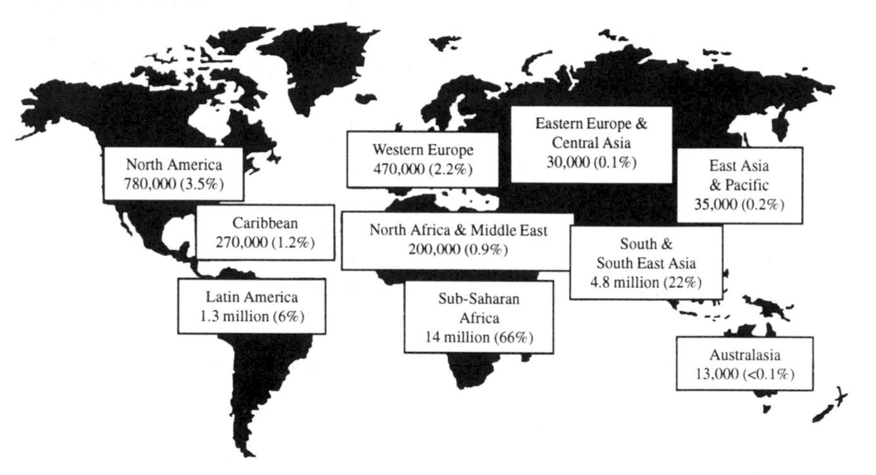

Source: WHO, WER 1996; 71:205-8

The situation is unstable as epidemics can explode, for example:

- In Bombay 50% of the sex workers have been found HIV infected within a short space of time;
- In the Ukraine in 1995 1.7% injecting drug users were HIV positive, 11 months later 56% were infected.

Western world

- HIV seroprevalence is increasing in young gay men in the USA and the United Kingdom (Adler, 1997);
- More women are becoming infected.

The United Kingdom

- In the UK, rates of infection are currently low and quite stable compared with other European countries, but there is regional variation;
- The prevalence in London is higher than in other parts of the country;
- There is more infection amongst drug users in Scotland than in England;
- The numbers of heterosexual men, women, and children infected is rising slowly;
- There have been over 4,000 reports of HIV infection in women (1997);
- Mother to child transmission is the major mode of infection for 85% of paediatric AIDS (1997);
- The numbers of children infected born to HIV-infected mothers continues to rise because HIV antenatal testing is not yet routinely offered and recommended.

These trends highlight the need for continuing vigilance and for HIV prevention work to be integrated into all health and social care settings.

Reports of HIV-1 infections and AIDS cases by exposure category: UK to end 1996

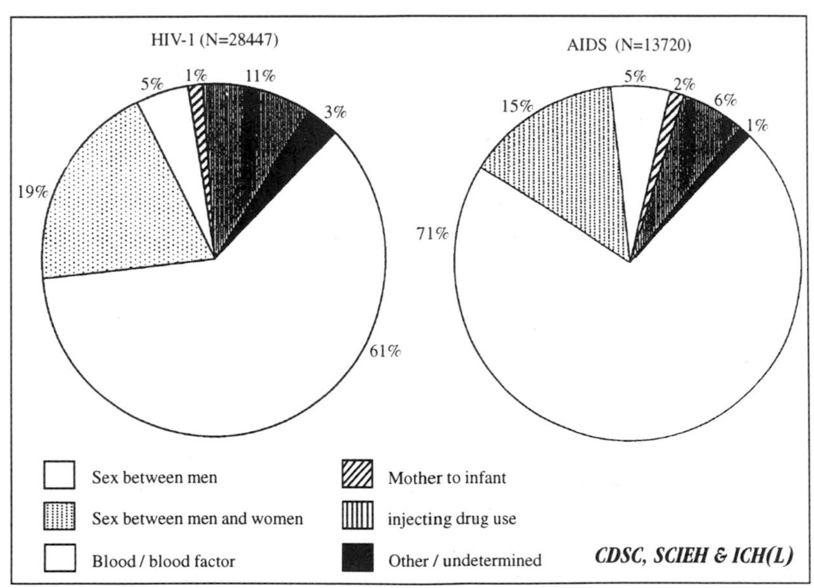

The profile of those "at risk" and infected with HIV influences attitudes to HIV testing, treatment, planning, and delivery of services. In England the low incidence of HIV infection amongst injecting drug users is due to safer drug use (needle exchanges – not sharing works), although not always safer sex. In Scotland (Edinburgh, Dundee) and Ireland (Dublin) there are considerable problems associated with HIV and the drug-using population.

The worldwide figures of HIV infection are relevant for the UK because;

- Increased leisure and business travel to and from areas of high incidence can result in people from the UK becoming infected abroad or visitors bringing HIV to the UK;
- Asylum seekers and migrants who come from areas of high incidence of HIV infection may come forward for testing or treatment, often only when they are acutely unwell;
- The movement of people within the European Union means that some infected drug users, from areas of high incidence in other European countries, present in the UK (especially London) for treatment;
- There are high rates of infection amongst some populations in the UK (e.g. sub-Sahara Africans);
- The rise in the incidence of HIV in eastern European countries may mean an increase in infected people coming to the UK from these countries as asylum seekers or economic migrants.

Although the current epidemic of HIV in the UK has not reached predicted proportions, a significant number of those infected with HIV remain undetected. Anonymous HIV antenatal screening in the United Kingdom (UK) suggests that 87% of women who are HIV positive in London and the South-East are unaware of their condition and thus can transmit HIV to their unborn children. The prevalence was found to be 1:250 and varies regionally (PHLS, 1996). These findings highlight the need for HIV antibody testing to be offered routinely in antenatal and family planning clinics to reduce the number of children avoidably infected (Scarlatti, 1996) and to offer treatment to HIV-infected women.

What is HIV?

HIV is a retrovirus (virus in which the genetic information is contained in the RNA instead of the DNA molecule). This virus is delicate and does not survive outside the body for more than minutes and thus, contrary to many myths, it is difficult to transmit. The virus is passed from one person to another through the exchange of body fluids. The highest concentration of the virus is found in blood, but HIV viral particles have been found in most body fluids.

Proven routes of transmission

- **Penetrative sexual contact** (anal, vaginal) by both active and passive sexual intercourse. The risk is greater for the receptive partner (male or female). Transmission is more likely where there is direct contact with the blood circulation (sexual intercourse associated with trauma, bleeding, or genital ulceration).
- Direct **inoculation of blood** from HIV-infected individuals (injecting drug users, contamination through needles or sharps). The risk of infection following a sharp's accident (needle stick or scalpel cut) has been shown world-wide to be 0.3% from a *known* infected person. The risks can vary according to the type of injury (if the inoculation is from a needle with a wide bore and the injury is deeper, the risk is higher).
- **Blood-transfusion-related transmission** is rarely seen in countries where donated blood is screened for HIV but may occur in isolated cases because of the "window period" for detection of antibodies. In the UK, *blood donations* have been routinely tested for HIV infection since 1985. People are discouraged from donating blood if they consider themselves to have been at risk. Information leaflets at donation centres are provided to help people identify their risk. Viral inactivation used for Factor VIII and IX concentrates (treatment of haemophilia) have halted this route of HIV transmission. Whole blood, on the other hand, cannot be heat treated and therefore there remains the very slight risk of transmission of infection from a blood transfusion.
- **Vertical transmission from mother to child *in utero* or perinatally.** The incidence of transmission of HIV from mother to unborn infant is lower in Europe than in Africa where the risk is higher due to co-infection with other sexually transmitted diseases, malnutrition, genital ulceration and through breast feeding.

EDUCING TRANSMISSION

, practice of safer sex between
ı and women;
en and men;
Women and women.

- Regular use of condoms reduces the risk of transmission but does not provide 100% protection;
- Not sharing needles and syringes by providing for needle exchange and disposal services for injecting drug users;
- Universal precautions (use of gloves, attention to practice – not resheathing needles) in health and other settings can reduce the risk of infection via inoculation of infected body fluids;
- Reducing vertical transmission from mother to unborn infant:

  Antenatal HIV screening should be offered to all pregnant women;

  Where the mother's HIV status is known prophylactic regimes of AZT during pregnancy can reduce the risk of HIV transmission to the infant *in utero* or at time of delivery from 25% to 13% (Johnstone, 1996);

  Delivery by elective Caesarean section is thought to reduce the risk of transmission by 50% in some studies, but it is not yet proven;

  Breast feeding by an HIV-infected mother doubles the risk of vertical transmission. Knowledge of HIV condition can enable mothers to refrain from breast feeding. In the Western world HIV-infected mothers are encouraged not to breast feed;

  Diagnosing and treating sexually transmitted diseases can reduce the spread of HIV by alerting individuals to the links between STDs and HIV.

Diagnosis of HIV infection (HIV antibody testing)

Some knowledge of the tests used for diagnosing HIV infection and information about where they are available is essential for social workers who deal with individuals who might be at risk of infection or who are considering testing.

The HIV antibody test

This is the most commonly available test for detection of the presence of antibodies to HIV (indicating that infection has taken place). It is sensitive and specific.

- It is a simple blood test (of 5mls) usually taken from an arm vein;
- Confirmation of positive antibody tests is made by other means of antibody detection (Western blotting and immunofluorescence). The result can be given within a few hours, although the time between testing and receiving results varies according to where the test is carried out;
- Testing is available through sexually transmitted diseases clinics, GP practices, free-standing anonymous testing services, antenatal clinics, and private fee-paying laboratories.

Early infection

- It can take the body up to three months (known as the "window period") to produce antibodies to HIV (markers detectable in blood by the HIV antibody test);
- During this period the individual is infectious but may not know that he/she is infected as antibodies may not yet be detectable by antibody test. A proportion of people (up to 50%) during this time develop a seroconversion-type illness;
- Immediately following initial infection, some of the protein products of viral replication (the virus) may be detectable in blood samples by a test called the HIV P24 antigen. This test is available in HIV specialist centres but is only used in particular circumstances to confirm infection before the development of antibodies which otherwise would not be detectable for up to three months.

Polymerase chain reaction (PCR) and viral load tests

- These tests detect the HIV virus itself (PCR) and the amount of circulating virus (viral load);
- The tests are important in special situations of early infection:

  Diagnosis of neonates and infants. The presence of detectable HIV antibodies acquired passively from the mother's circulation *in utero* may persist up until the

infant is 18 months of age and may not represent true HIV infection. PCR-based techniques can help predict infection within a few days of birth but have to be repeated on two further occasions.

For individuals who may be **seroconverting** (showing that they are or have just become infected with HIV). These individuals if diagnosed soon after infection can commence antiretroviral treatment which may halt infection. This is not proven to date but is "biologically plausible".

For **occupational risk** for HIV from needle or sharps incidence in health care settings these sensitive tests can help in difficult treatment decisions. Department of Health "Guidelines on Post-Exposure Prophylaxis for Health Care workers Occupationally Exposed to HIV" (UK Health Departments June 1997) now recommend immediate treatment with combination antiretroviral treatment after an occupational risk.

NATURAL HISTORY OF HIV INFECTION

SEROCONVERSION

Following infection with HIV, 50-60% of individuals experience what is known as a seroconversion illness with flu-like symptoms (fever, sore throat, swollen glands, headaches, rash). Seroconversion usually occurs one to two months following infection and is not always easily identified.

CLINICALLY ASYMPTOMATIC STAGE

It is believed that there is no truly asymptomatic phase in HIV infection as viral replication continues from time of infection.

- Some individuals may be well with no symptoms, have a high CD4 count (indication of good immune function), and have a low rate of viral replication;
- Others may have a high CD4 count and fairly high viral load;
- Yet others may have a high level of circulating virus, and prophylactic antiviral therapy might be indicated for them at this early stage.

This stage can last for many years when individuals may be well with few if any clinical symptoms. At this stage individuals who have not been diagnosed may be unaware of the presence of HIV infection. At times some symptoms may appear in a mild form and are often hard to distinguish from commonly occurring problems that might prompt individuals to consult their general practitioners (skin problems, thrush). During this phase there is continued viral replication and CD4 counts gradually fall over time. The immune system weakens as the viral load increases.

Symptomatic HIV infection and advanced HIV disease

During this stage:

- There can be clinical symptoms which can be non-specific (weight loss, sweats, lethargy);
- Individuals may develop more specific and persistent symptoms such as mouth problems (ulcers, thrush, gum diseases, and dental problems), skin conditions (shingles, rashes, scabies, warts, and psoriasis), genital symptoms (warts, abnormal smears, recurrent herpes, and thrush) and gastrointestinal problems (diarrhoea);
- There may be symptoms of very advanced disease (Kaposi's sarcoma, TB, PCP, lymphomas);
- Decisions need to be made by patients and doctors about starting prophylactic treatments for opportunistic infections and antiretroviral therapy to reduce viral replication.

A diagnosis of AIDS indicates that the immune system is very compromised with CD4 counts usually below 200 cells mm. Clinical classifications of disease were developed by the centers for disease control (CDC) in Atlanta, Georgia, USA (1985) and revised to include women with cervical cancer and for children in 1994 (see Appendix).

Monitoring

HIV infection destroys an individual's immune system over time. The rate of destruction will vary from person to person. The reasons why some patients progress more quickly to AIDS than others are still the focus of research but may be related to the type of virus they have acquired (HIV1/2 a,b,c,d) and the person's genetic make-up affecting their individual response to HIV. Medical monitoring is now very important because even when a person appears well (asymptomatic) with a relatively high CD4 count there may be rapid replication of virus. The monitoring of HIV-infected people in specialist HIV clinics includes:

- History taking (to clarify natural history of HIV infection);
- Clinical examination (to detect symptoms);
- Laboratory tests (to monitor disease progression);
- Psychosocial assessment (to offer support in managing illness and in making decisions about commencing treatment).

LABORATORY MONITORING

When individuals become infected with HIV the virus primarily infects cells of the immune system called the CD4 lymphocytes (T helper cells). These cells, in the normal course of events, fight infection and provide immunity to some diseases. The CD4 helper cells (the very mechanisms that should protect the body against infection) are destroyed over time by HIV.

- Until about 1996 the measurement of CD4 lymphocyte cells has been the main monitoring test. The normal range of CD4 lymphocytes is between 400 and 1,000 in non-infected individuals. In people with HIV, there is a steady decline in the CD4 count, and the rate of this decline varies from individual to individual and also within the same individual;
- Viral load testing is now carried out at specialist HIV centres. The test indicates how active viral replication is in the individual's body and is now used alongside the CD4 counts as an indication of when to introduce or change antiretroviral therapy.

In specialised HIV clinics, monitoring CD4 counts and viral load replication, together with clinical evaluation, gives patients and doctors more information and better guidance about when to start, switch, or stop antiretoviral treatments (BHIVA, 1997). Current dilemmas centre upon whether to start treatment early if an individual has a high viral load, and postpone introduction of treatment if the viral load is low. These uncertainties will only become clearer over time.

TREATMENT

HIV is a serious, complex, medical condition involving many different specialities (infectious diseases, genito-urinary and thoracic medicine, neurology, dermatology, virology, immunology) as well as other health care professionals (pharmacists, dieticians, nurses, social workers, and counsellors) all contributing to comprehensive care. From a medical point of view, specialist expertise and wide experience are required to:

- Diagnose complex clinical presentations;
- Interpret monitoring tests;
- Make decisions about when to start, change, or stop antiretroviral therapies.

Many of the new combinations of antiretroviral therapies involve taking large numbers of drugs and in different concentrations, with or without food, at different times of the day. Some drugs have side-effects (nausea, diarrhoea, peripheral neuropathy) and many of the drugs have complex interactions and cannot be taken with other medicines. A newer group of antiretroviral drugs (protease inhibitors) offer promise in antiretroviral treatment. Compliance with taking these drugs is vital in order to reduce the chance of developing resistance, to maximise effectiveness, and to deal with any side-effects, many of which are reversible. It is also possible that individuals may be able to transmit a resistant strain of HIV virus to other people. Such issues are now emerging and need to be addressed with patients.

Social workers need to have some understanding of how patients' daily lives are affected by these complex treatment regimes so that appropriate support can be offered.

CONCLUSIONS

In the early years of the epidemic, individuals with HIV infection often presented as acutely unwell, dying soon after an AIDS diagnosis. HIV is now viewed as a more chronic condition with periods of acute illness. Patients nowadays survive multiple opportunistic infections and are living with fluctuating periods of health.

It has been found that early diagnosis and follow-up at specialist treatment centres by experienced physicians are key factors to optimal treatment and survival (Kitahata et al., 1996). There is now, in 1998, greater optimism about the efficacy of the increasing variety of antiretroviral treatments available, used mainly in combination therapy. Whether these treatments should be offered at an early or late stage in HIV infection is still an aspect of some medical debate. Answers to some of these uncertainties will emerge over time through the participation of patients in drugs trials, cohort studies, and regular medical follow-up by clinicians. Through drug trials, patients also may have early access to new drugs before they are licensed for open prescription.

Health and social care professionals can contribute to patient survival by being aware of the important factors that affect diagnosis and treatment of HIV infection. If well informed, social workers will be able to deal sensitively and effectively with the concerns raised by their clients and encourage them to attend and continue to attend for medical care. It is important that individuals with any serious medical condition have access to expert medical treatment, but it is equally important that they have the assistance that they need to live their lives as normally as possible.

Dilemmas and practice issues

INTRODUCTION

Dilemmas related to HIV infection may present in daily social work practice in a variety of settings including:

- Who should raise and address HIV issues?;
- Where is it best done?;
- When are appropriate times to do this?;
- What, if any, issues does HIV raise for clients and social workers that are different from other medical conditions?

The contribution social workers can make towards HIV prevention and in addressing the needs of those infected and affected by HIV can be more clearly defined once practice issues are identified.

SOME DILEMMAS FACING SOCIAL WORKERS

Most of the dilemmas discussed below are not new to social work practitioners, but can be further complicated by HIV infection. These include:

- Concerns about raising issues that could **cause tensions in the social worker:client relationship**, including:
  - Discomfort in raising and talking about sex, sexual behaviour, sexual orientation, or drug use;
  - Fears about the personally intrusive nature of such discussions;
  - Sensitivity about appearing judgemental or appearing to show discrimination because of the perceptions of HIV disease;
  - Lack of confidence about how best to approach the subject.
- **Reluctance to raise HIV**, even when it is relevant to do so with those "at risk". Assumptions should not be made about people's risk or knowledge about HIV infection. Some people are "at risk" and do not know it. Others may know about being "at risk" or being infected but may not wish to tell others (family, sexual partners, GPs);

- Conflicts between the **rights of individuals and those of the "public good"**. (Clients have a right to privacy and confidentiality, but this might put others at risk for HIV without knowing it.)

  Examples

  The rights of a child and mother may be in conflict if a pregnant woman at "high risk" of HIV refuses HIV testing;

  A parent refuses to allow her HIV-infected child to be given drug treatment;

  A bisexual or homosexual man refuses to tell his partner that he is infected;

- **Accessing those most at risk of HIV** (young, sexually active, and of childbearing age) can be difficult.

  Many of those infected are single (generally a healthy population) and are usually infrequent users of health or social care services;

  Some may be alienated from the natural support network of family or friends (through lifestyle);

  Others have concerns about disclosure to those who would be in a position to offer support (health and social services, family) because of fears of breaches of confidentiality.

- A diagnosis of HIV may **reveal a hidden lifestyle** (homosexuality, bisexuality) or activities associated with behaviours outside the "acceptable" norm (drug use, extra-marital relationships). Social workers may have to:

  Face difficulties and conflicts in addressing health concerns and prevention of HIV transmission because of the illicit nature of activities (drug use, sexual abuse, prostitution, and under-age sex);

  Ask probing, explicit questions about sexual behaviour when answers might be required to clarify and assess HIV risks with individuals and couples (fostering, adoption, sexual abuse).

- **Drug users** are a hard-to-reach population. HIV can complicate pre-existing difficulties for those "at risk" of or infected by HIV. Social workers may be deterred from raising HIV issues with this population for a number of moral and practical reasons:

  The illegal aspects of using and dealing and the associated lifestyle mean that many drug users are reluctant to engage with social workers;

  If a drug-using mother has pre-existing child protection issues she may be afraid that HIV will increase the chances of her child being taken into care. She may be reluctant to be tested for HIV, and if she has HIV may not be willing to engage with professionals from whom help and support might be gained;

- Drug users are often not receptive to receiving health information. Those with HIV infection have been found to be more willing to consult medical practitioners (Mounteney & Shapiro, 1998). Some wish to protect their health whilst others for social and personal reasons feel there is no point in extra medical care;
- Decisions often have to be made about balancing HIV treatment with efforts to deal with addiction;
- Many drug users are co-infected with HIV and hepatitis C, and sometimes also hepatitis B. Their overall prognosis may be worse from both HIV and hepatitis points of view. The client and social worker can both feel overwhelmed. Dilemmas can arise as to which issue should receive priority;
- Health and safety issues in relation to needles and other works must be addressed. This means giving advice about needle exchanges and disposal services to reduce transmission of HIV. In some circumstances this can pose a dilemma about encouraging injecting behaviour.

- HIV infection has an **impact on relationships**. It affects the health, personal, and social life of not only the infected individual but those closely connected with that person (family, sexual partner, colleagues, friends, and acquaintances) and can raise dilemmas about:
  - Who is the "index" client (the partners, children, or family members may have more problems about HIV than the client);
  - The fears (stigma, homophobia) underlying some relationship tensions (between the client and family, employer/employee);
  - The impact of HIV in prolonging or cutting short relationships. Some stay together because of HIV, despite all difficulties (guilt, fear of leaving, loyalty). For others a break is precipitated (fear of infection, illness, role reversal, stigma) by a diagnosis of HIV;
- Dilemmas about **who is the family** can impinge on decisions about provision of care for the patient. HIV has been a major factor in bringing about a more readily accepted redefinition of the family, from that of "origin" (the birth family) to that of "choice" (individuals chosen to be the family) (Bor & Miller, 1995).
  - A greater acceptance of same-sex couples has been brought about largely through gay men having to access health care and revealing more about their lifestyle. Health and welfare agencies have become used to dealing with same-sex couples issues (next of kin, who is the major carer, who makes decisions – family of origin or family of choice?);

Single people with HIV, living away from home, are often more dependent on friends than family. Issues about next-of-kin can arise, especially in the terminal stages of illness;

Conflicts between the rights and responsibilities of the family of origin and family of choice may appear, particularly when the patient is terminally ill or following death (next of kin, who is included in funeral arrangements);

Some infected people do not tell parents about HIV in an attempt to "protect them", for fear of being rejected, or because they have not discussed other sensitive issues (drug use, homosexuality, extramarital relationship).

In other instances families who were previously distant can be brought closer through disclosure of the HIV infection and resulting illness.

- Issues surrounding **disclosure** of status and confidentiality are sensitive due to stigma and discrimination experienced by people with HIV and their close contacts. The dilemmas include:

The reluctance on the part of individuals to disclose their HIV status has in some instances to be addressed by social workers, which can sometimes be perceived as conflicting with the social worker's role as advocate against discrimination. Encouraging clients to inform pertinent others can be critical to:

- prevention of HIV transmission;
- obtaining optimal treatment and care (GP, dentist);
- accessing practical help (social security benefits and housing).

Issues of confidentiality are frequently raised by clients. Although HIV poses no especially new issues for social workers, clients may be more sensitive about breaches of confidentiality due to stigma and fears of discrimination. There should be clarity between the client and social worker about which issues might be problematic if not shared with others (for example, telling a GP or housing department about HIV to access appropriate care). Being explicit about the source of infection is not necessary in most circumstances;

Who needs to know the HIV diagnosis, and for what reason, is central to discussions with clients, and may pose difficulties for social workers and clients alike. Examples include:

i Partners or children "at risk" of HIV who are uninformed about the client's HIV status;

ii Reluctance on the part of parents to disclose a child's or their own HIV status to nurseries, schools, and child-minders due to anticipated hostile reactions (refusal to have the child, preventing children from different families playing together);

iii The desire for secrecy may conflict with the best interests of the child (for instance, if teachers are unaware of HIVinfection which could contribute to behavioural or learning difficulties);

iv Fears that "social workers might remove my child if I tell them I have HIV";

v Adults with HIV may fear that disclosure will result in discrimination and prejudice from employers, neighbours, friends, health and social care professionals.

- **Divisions of work between the adult disability and children and families social work teams** can lead to dilemmas about which team should be involved when more than one person in the family has HIV infection (child and adult, or an infected adult with uninfected children).

  If both teams are involved, lack of clarity about which team has major responsibility can result in care being fragmented;

  Issues surrounding payment for care packages may arise when two teams (adult and children and families) are involved and can delay provision of necessary services. These can be further complicated when the cost of the package is also shared with the mental health team and health authority;

  Sometimes too many workers are involved, with overlapping tasks and duplication adding to the confusion for both the family and the workers.

- **Residential care r**aises dilemmas about if, when, and how best to raise and address HIV. Ensuring that children and young people in care, or leaving care, have adequate knowledge about HIV infection and how to protect themselves is, it seems, a responsibility of social workers. Social workers can be deterred from initiating this activity and taking a proactive stance due to:

  Difficulties of initiating discussion with adolescents about sensitive issues (sex, death, pregnancy);

  A perception that they lack the knowledge (about HIV) to answer questions which might be asked. This can lead to avoidance in addressing adolescent sexuality, its connection with HIV, and other sexually transmitted diseases;

  Dilemmas in relation to confidentiality when considering who needs to know about an infected individual (other residents, staff, children themselves, and the natural parents) or about someone at risk (rape, abuse).

- **Duty to care** can pose dilemmas for social workers:
  - When a child has been sexually abused the "duty to care" may present dilemmas for social workers about when to raise concerns about HIV amongst the many other important issues;
  - Those leaving residential care at age 16 may be particularly vulnerable and at risk of acquiring HIV infection as they seek security in relationships, financial stability, and a home.
- Dilemmas may arise for social service managers as to whether or not there should be **specialist HIV social work posts**. Issues include:
  - As special HIV funding becomes more limited it is less likely that specialist posts will be a chosen option. On the other hand it is undoubtedly easier to gain expertise quickly when there is an opportunity to concentrate on a speciality area. HIV care is complicated and perhaps specialist posts are still needed in areas of high prevalence for adults, children, and families;
  - The rationale for this book is the belief that all social workers need a working knowledge of HIV so that raising the issue can be integrated into generic teams and day-to-day practice;
  - Social workers from both specialist and generic teams inevitably become involved as funding for HIV respite facilities and other voluntary services increasingly requires Care Needs Assessments to be carried out.

PRACTICE ISSUES

A variety of practice issues arise when dealing with individuals, couples, and families with HIV infection, especially women and children, where diagnosis and treatment can, in some circumstances, be more complex.

1. Any concerns about the risks of **transmission** of HIV infection in the workplace must initially be addressed. Knowledge about risks and how to deal with them affects the level of confidence social workers have in their ability to deal with difficult situations.

- Staff may worry about becoming infected (accidents,bites, wounds). Policies and practices are similar to those for hepatitis B and need to be in place to deal with instances as they occur. The Health and Safety at Work Act 1974 covers the main issues for staff;

- Staff may worry about other children becoming infected (bites and physical violence);
- Clients and their contacts may worry about the risks of infection and their concerns must be addressed (risk of household transmission between siblings and others);
- Parents of HIV-infected children (whose immune function is compromised) may worry about the risks to their child's health of picking up infections from other children;
- Parents of uninfected children may have concerns about their children being exposed to HIV through accidents.

2. The point at which individuals with HIV infection can **access social work** services depends on

- The threshold in the local borough for social work interventions;
- Which team will provide services (children and families, adult disability, elderly, mental health). The mental health team may consider the problem to be physical health (HIV), whereas the HIV team consider that it falls under mental health expertise;
- The patient's willingness to accept help and be referred to appropriate services. Some individuals manage alone with considerable difficulties until there is a crisis. Most people do not like the intrusion of services into their lives unless it is absolutely necessary. Other patients may request help before they are disabled enough to qualify for the services they seek;
- Occasionally individuals try to gain access to services by feigning that they have HIV infection. Thus confirmation from a medical centre of the patient's HIV infection should always be sought prior to initiating a service.

3. If patients and carers require help in times of crisis it may take some time for social services to respond due to a variety of reasons (pressure of work, allocation procedures)

- Shorter hospital admissions and discharge planning require care needs assessments to be done at short notice;

- Liaison between the different health and social careworkers involves letters and other necessary paper work before services can be instituted;
- Services may be required from HIV specialist or general adult disabilities teams with waiting lists, differing priorities, and a need to ration all services;
- With children the case is often not allocated unless there is a crisis.

4. Fluctuating health and disability in patients with HIV infection (periods of feeling well and being independent, and others of being unwell and needing help) can make it more difficult to plan and manage care packages.

- The symptoms experienced by patients can lead to a variety of disabilities, ranging from less obvious difficulties (night sweats, rashes, generalised fatigue) to those that are obviously disabling (blindness, extreme fatigue, constant diarrhoea, inability to control physical movement, and difficulty in eating);
- HIV disease progression is not always predictable and varies greatly from person to person. HIV may manifest itself in a variety of systems and organs in the body, and symptoms themselves can also fluctuate over time (seriously unwell, and then, some weeks later, be able to return to work);
- Impairment is on a continuum from inability to work full time to severe restrictions in ability to perform activities of daily living. With new treatments people may require varying degrees of care over a longer time frame in order to continue to live in the community;
- Decisions about when to be actively involved with an individual or family and when to withdraw are dictated not only by the changing needs of the patient but also by the threshold for accessing care set down by the borough in which the social worker is located;
- The fluctuating health of a parent with HIV can make it difficult to help children deal with this, including the possiblity of being orphaned. It can be made more difficult when those children are infected themselves.

5. Although a **proactive approach** works best, in practice this is not always possible.

- The optimal time to include social work help is before people become physically or mentally impaired or require comprehensive needs assessments to the extent that it affects their decision-making and limits choices;
- Care management, in most social services, does not allow for this to happen. Some cases will not be allocated unless a comprehensive needs assessment is required;
- Patients may see duty social workers most of the time due to systems of case allocation;
- The need to be proactive is particularly important in the case of families. Health may change very quickly (children might need care when a mother needs urgent admission to hospital).

6. Through the provision of **practical services** (accessing DSS benefits, disabled parking badges, taxi cards, travel passes, home help) a trusting relationship between social worker and client can develop which makes future contact easier.

- Over time, more-sensitive issues can begin to be addressed (making wills, planning for future care of children, informing sexual partners and family, and death);
- Financial and practical help can reduce patients' fears of how they might cope in the future if they become ill;
- Assisting with suitable practical issues (housing and benefits) is especially important as patients become unwell. As they become more disabled it may not be possible for them to be discharged home and they could unnecessarily spend longer time in hospital. This may particularly be the case with drug users and families living in sub-optimal accommodation prior to the development of illness.

7. The **Department of Social Security** (DSS) regulations regarding eligibility for some benefits change from time to time, and this has an impact on patients' lives and expectations. For example, DSS benefits regulations regarding Income Support, Incapacity Benefit, and Disabled Living Allowance are being applied more stringently in 1998. Social workers and their welfare rights colleagues can help to disseminate information to health care teams and patients to reduce conflicts over unrealistic expectations.

8. Local social service departments need to know the **pattern of HIV in their locality** (single men, drug users, affected children) and to consider future needs of potential clients. Hospital teams can link patients with local social services which also helps to clarify present and future needs. Examples include:

- Whilst helping a woman access telephone installation or payment of the rental, information can be given about other services available if required. A relationship can begin to develop reducing anxiety and making it easier for contact to be made in the future;
- Helping access nursery placements or child-minding assistance can be a valuable entrée to the more sensitive discussion about future care of children for an HIV-infected mother.

9. The pre-terminal stages of HIV illness may last for some time, with fluctuating degrees of mental and physical impairment. Provision of care to young, terminally ill men and women (who may or may not have the support of family around, or only in a limited way) can be complicated.

- Clarifying patients' and carers' wishes and beliefs in advance of the onset of the terminal phase of illness enables appropriate care to be considered and planned for (dying at home or in hospital);
- Terminal care at home requires planning and involvement with different agencies. Community services (social services, general practitioners, community nurse specialists, health visitors) need to have good working links with specialist HIV-treating centres and voluntary organisations to provide optimum care;

- Case conferences, discharge planning meetings, and regular review meetings between health and social care teams are a way of facilitating efficient working relationships;
- The social worker, as care manager, is in a key position to co-ordinate the various services.

10. Providing care to a **family** is more complex than to a single individual, from the medical and social point of view. Finding the right way forward is not easy because there is no "blue-print" to suit every situation. Helping parents to make difficult decisions about a range of complex issues is an important task:

- Pregnancy and termination of pregnancy;
- HIV testing of children;
- Treatment of HIV-infected children;
- Future care of children;
- Parents accessing care;
- Safety of children. Where there are tensions regarding the child's right to treatment or the parents' right to make decisions about their child, social workers can draw on their experience of the Children's Act 1989 or consult the child protection team.

11. Psychiatric illness and neurological impairment are not unusual in HIV infection. It can be difficult to distinguish pre-existing personality difficulties from psychiatric illness resulting from HIV or related opportunistic infections:

- Some individuals may present with a cluster of psychiatric symptoms. It is not clear which symptom is related to:
  - i personality traits;
  - ii the change in personal situation;
  - iii HIV infection in the brain (acute brain infections, tumours, or neuropathy.
- Personality disorders, behavioural difficulties, and other psychiatric illnesses can be complicated or exacerbated by

HIV either early on in the adjustment period or later as health deteriorates;

- Patients may develop psychiatric illnesses as a result of a diagnosis of HIV (depression, anxiety, acute psychotic episodes) and need expert mental health assessment and treatment;
- These complex cases require liaison between all the different agencies to enable the individual to obtain the required care and assistance:
  - i Specialist assessment, treatment, and management are required with several teams working together (HIV, psychiatric, social work);
  - ii It is not uncommon for three different social work teams to be involved: adult disability, children and family, and mental health;
  - iii At times, different social service teams may be reluctant to become involved, due to limited resources.
- The management of patients with psychiatric illness or HIV neurological impairment is rarely straightforward.Although they may need home support, their needs may be hard to define. Sufficiently flexible services may not exist (patients physically well, but mentally unstable).

12. The death of a person from HIV infection does not necessarily mean the end of the problem

- Those connected with that person may themselves be infected, or they may fear that they are infected or may be isolated through fear of stigma;
- Often the cause of death is not discussed with neighbours or friends (especially if parents live in communities very different to large urban centres where their adult child lived);
- Some elderly parents or partners may have contact with social workers through other areas of need (housing, home care) yet may be unable to talk about their child's HIV.

13. Working with people from diverse ethnic backgrounds is an important aspect of HIV care.

- Many people with HIV from different ethnic backgrounds come from cultures where attitudes to sexuality, birth, and death differ radically from those of the host country;
- Their situations may be complicated by immigration difficulties. In these cases it is sometimes hard to know whether to focus first on health-related issues or other more practical concerns (deportation);
- Although some understanding of the culture from which the person comes is helpful, information can be gained from clients by enquiring about their cultural traditions, acknowledging the differences of the host culture, and eliciting their views and beliefs about HIV;
- It is debatable as to whether patients from different ethnic backgrounds should be dealt with by workers from the same culture. There is no clear answer to this. In some cases patients welcome someone from their own background. In other cases this is not so (some people from Uganda and other African countries refuse to meet a worker from their own country);
- In central London people from eastern Europe (Ukraine, Bosnia, Russia) are becoming more frequent users of health and social services, as are those from southern Europe (Italy, France, Spain). Patient access to services is complicated by rules about entitlement to Nation Health Service care, and DSS benefits under conditions of habitual residence;
- Language barriers can complicate the provision of care, particularly discussion of sensitive issues (sex, child care, death), especially when translators have to be used. If the translators are relatives it may further inhibit discussion and is often not appropriate;
- No assumptions should be made about the influence of ethnicity, gender, and cultural context. Non-indigenous peoples' views and beliefs vary greatly and are affected by age, class, gender, and the length of time domiciled in the UK.

14. Particular difficulties can arise for social workers because of the impact of HIV on those working in the field. **Maintaining a neutral stance** in social work practice is always a necessary aim. It can be difficult in HIV because of

- Over-identification with young patients and families of similar age and circumstances who are facing seemingly overwhelming difficulties. The risks of sexual transmission apply to the general population – not only our clients – and thus may trigger personal reactions for social workers;
- Differences in beliefs, lifestyle, cultural and ethical values which impinge on the social worker-client relationship are brought to the fore through dealing with sex, having children, and beliefs about life and death that are more common in HIV.

CONCLUDING POINTS

Social workers can play an active part in preventing and helping to diagnose HIV in all settings merely by raising HIV more routinely among the other issues that they address (drug use, sexual abuse, and "failing to thrive" children).

Despite all the dilemmas and practical challenges, social workers are well placed to address a wide range of issues connected with HIV infection with their clients. Identifying dilemmas and practice issues are the first steps toward addressing HIV in a realistic way. Tensions between the individual and public good are ever-present in HIV and are issues most familiar to social workers (child care, elderly, mentally ill). Social workers have to find ways to use and develop their skills in dealing with HIV by incorporating it into both statutory work and that which is outside the prescribed roles. Offering practical advice and help to individuals may well provide an entrée to the discussion of more-difficult issues. In the authors' experience it is the approach used to clients, rather than the gender and ethnic origin, that is instrumental in helping those whose beliefs and backgrounds are different. Ongoing supervision and ready access to consultation are valuable and important.

The next chapters present some ideas about how to incorporate HIV issues into daily practice.

Counselling interventions for social workers in HIV

INTRODUCTION

"Counselling" (to varying degrees) is inextricably part of the social work task with a focus on:

- Identifying needs and concerns of individuals and families (Care Needs Assessments);
- Clarifying what practical community support and financial benefits are available;
- Providing emotional support to clients and those closely connected with them;
- Providing information about:
  - HIV illness;
  - Transmission and prevention;
  - Services available for testing, treatment, and care.

The acceptance of counselling as a discrete or integral social work activity in social service departments varies from borough to borough throughout the country and from setting to setting where social workers are based. Nevertheless, individual social workers have found ways to integrate counselling into everyday practice. The HIV teams and specialist posts have contributed considerable expertise in this area, especially where there has been opportunity for a degree of autonomy. Social workers employed in voluntary agencies have different roles and tasks and are not constrained to the same extent in relation to "counselling".

The NHS and Community Care Act of 1990 underlines Care Needs Assessments as a basic social work task. Assessment, the first step in any intervention, is central to the social work role and is considered in detail in *The Art of Assessment* (Middleton, 1997). The separation of counselling from other tasks increases the dilemmas and reluctance on the part of some social workers to become involved in discussions about HIV. The recent Department of Health guidelines on HIV antibody testing are to be welcomed. The word "discussion" replaces "counselling" prior to HIV testing (DoH, 1996) and this helps to dispel some of the myths surrounding HIV counselling.

This chapter suggests guidelines for how counselling about HIV in the social work setting can be integrated into everyday practice. The approach to counselling described has been adapted from the techniques of the Milan Associates (Cecchin, 1989). It enables social workers to develop a map of therapeutic practice and to conceptualise problems in a systemic framework (Miller & Bor, 1988). These guidelines can be adapted to situations other than HIV which social workers face, whether it is assessment of need for an individual in crisis or dealing with other difficult situations (child abuse, domestic violence, truancy).

WHY COUNSELLING IS IMPORTANT IN HIV INFECTION

Counselling is important in HIV prevention and management because:

- HIV is incurable, life long and infectious;
- Information must be elicited and given about transmission, prevention, diagnosis, treatment, and care;
- Information about HIV can be uncertain and confusing as the natural history evolves and new treatments are introduced;
- HIV affects relationships (sexual partners, family, friends, and employers);
- HIV can be stigmatising, resulting in secrets, isolation, and discrimination;
- The population most affected is largely, but not exclusively, young, sexually active, and of child-bearing age;
- Normal life cycle stages may be upset with reversals of hopes, expectations, and roles for patients and their close contacts (retiring early, choosing whether to have children, premature death, dependency at an early age, resuming a caring role for adult children, and children dying before parents);
- Children may be infected, affected, and orphaned, and their needs must be addressed;

- Preparation for changes in health and early death can be considered and plans formulated;
- Patients may need help in making informed decisions about a wide range of issues (choosing between conventional and alternative medicine, participating in drug trials, embarking on travel, migration, having children, making wills, living wills, and arrangements for guardianship of children left behind);
- Some particular bereavement issues can occur because of perceived and actual stigma (children dying before parents, secrecy, isolation, multiple loss, infection of sexual partners and children.

Definition of counselling

Counselling about HIV can be defined for social workers in any setting as a discussion or dialogue with an individual or individuals to:

- Give and elicit information;
- Identify and address concerns, wishes, and beliefs;
- Enable informed decision-making;
- Make appropriate referrals.

Counselling interventions, at all stages of HIV infection, should aim to create a balance between provoking anxiety (discussion about uncertainty about HIV condition for those not yet tested, or fears about disclosure for those infected) and defining the reality of the individual's situation (certainty of having HIV and being faced with illness, disclosure to others for access to services, prevention of transmission).

Guiding principles, aims, and task of counselling

Being clear about the aims and principles of counselling in relation to HIV can help reduce misunderstandings with clients and their contacts and helps to focus the work.

SOME GUIDING COUNSELLING PRINCIPLES

- Make no assumptions about an individual's knowledge, concerns, beliefs, and wishes;
- Recognise that everything said has an impact, thus words must be used carefully;
- Maintain some neutrality and be non-judgemental;
- Avoid giving false reassurance by answering honestly, and where answers are not known, explaining this.

AIMS OF COUNSELLING

Aims of counselling about HIV in the context of social work practice are to:

- Raise the subject of HIV appropriately, with an emphasis on prevention of transmission, and identification of those at risk of HIV infection;
- Elicit the extent of understanding about HIV (how it is transmitted, its implications for future health, treatment opportunities);
- Identify and address immediate concerns;
- Help individuals and families cope with the implications of transmittable, incurable infection (stigma, discrimination, reversals of hopes and expectations, disclosure to others, methods of prevention);
- Facilitate informed decision-making by the client;
- Consider with clients further actions which need to be taken (encouraging the individual to disclose HIV to others who might be "at risk" of the infection);
- Adopt a "proactive" stance when possible by anticipating difficulties (poor housing, lack of finance, mobility difficulties);
- Help clients and those close to them prepare for future changes by identifying concerns and clarify wishes and beliefs (dying at home, in hospital, hospice, care of dependent children). This can save time and prevent potential difficulties;
- Facilitate referral for specialist follow-up (to GP, specialist HIV unit, psychiatric assessment, family or couple work, or to a voluntary organisation).

COUNSELLING TASKS FOR SOCIAL WORKERS

Integrating counselling about a range of issues (child care, managing to live independently) into information giving, and provision of practical help is a key task. Specifically these include:

- Providing information about HIV transmission, prevention, diagnosis, treatment, and care. Social workers do not have to be fully informed about all details but need the confidence to distinguish between myths and realities. Knowledge of accurate, updated information (or where to access this), especially about treatments available for HIV infection, facilitates raising the issue more confidently;
- Enabling access to specialist resources for HIV testing, diagnosis, and treatment (general practitioner, HIV-testing clinics, specialist HIV care, antenatal clinics);
- Advocating and assisting with practical help on behalf of individuals for a range of issues (benefits, housing, accessing legal help, transport, and other necessities of daily living);
- Carrying out Care Needs Assessments and making referrals to appropriate voluntary or statutory organisations;
- Making initial assessments and liaising with approved mental health social workers under the Mental Health Act 1983 for those individuals with psychiatric problems or HIV dementia who are a danger to themselves or others;
- Helping individuals and families deal with relationship issues (making, ending, maintaining relationships, disclosure, dealing with declining health, loneliness, isolation) by introducing new perspectives to patients' problems. This can be done by linking ideas about how the individual coped with difficult events in the past and how these personal resources can be harnessed in the current situation;
- Liaising as key worker with medical practitioners and other social carers is essential as there are often many multidisciplinary issues;
- Balancing reality (that HIV is incurable and can be transmitted) with hope (there are now more-effective treatments) is a task underlying all counselling about HIV.

CASE EXAMPLES

In the following three case examples the individuals requested practical help from social services. In responding to these requests the social workers were able to begin to deal with relationship difficulties. The main tasks were to;

- Consider the stage of HIV infection the patient has reached;
- Clarify who else, important to the patient, knows about the HIV infection, and consider any agencies or individuals who should be informed;
- Consider relevant legal and ethical issues;
- Identify and assess psychological, social, and emotional issues that might affect the patient;
- Identify and mobilise the resources necessary to meet the client's needs;
- Assess the level of care needed.

CASE ONE. "AN INDEPENDENT GAY MAN"

John Brown is a 48-year-old gay man who is managing to continue his work as a solicitor. He has had HIV for 10 years but has been suffering from quite severe fatigue. He drives a car and approached his social worker for help with obtaining a disabled parking disc. He has commenced a combination of antiretroviral therapies which require monitoring at the hospital on a regular basis.

ISSUES FOR CONSIDERATION

- Helping access a disabled drivers disc;
- Identification of current and future concerns;
- Assessing wishes and needs;
- Ascertaining who else knows about the HIV (GP, family, friends, employer);
- Confirming what medical care the patient is receiving;
- Clarifying to whom the patient would turn if he needed help in the future;
- Informing him of what help is available from social services and how it can be accessed;
- Obtaining a letter of diagnosis from the doctor.

Case two. A Ugandan woman and her family

In contrast, Mary, a 30-year-old Ugandan woman with advanced HIV infection has three children under eight years. She has been referred by the health visitor for help with child minding for the baby aged 18 months and access to a nursery place for the three-year-old. It appears that she is reluctant to attend the hospital for a number of reasons. Some of these are of a practical nature but there are others which are more complex.

Issues for consideration

- Ascertaining Mary's stage of HIV infection and forming a liaison with her treatment centre;
- Establishing if she has a husband/partner or whether she is a single parent;
- Assessing her entitlements to benefits;
- Clarifying her immigration position;
- Finding a balance between offering the help that she is requesting and starting to explore some of the more difficult issues (care of the children should she become ill and need hospitalisation);
- Consider who else knows about her HIV and whom she is willing to tell (child minder, nursery school, GP, health visitor, partner);
- Identifying next-of-kin;
- Clarifying the HIV status of the children, whether or not they have had HIV tests and the mother's view about this.

Case three. Drug user with HIV

Jane, aged 29, has been an injecting drug-user for many years. She was found to be infected with HIV at a late stage of disease when she had an episode of pneumonia which did not respond to normal treatment. The GP was managing her drug use with methadone and after some time persuaded her to attend a specialist HIV unit. She has a five-year-old daughter. The local health visitor had met her daughter Cassie through the GP, but no social worker had hitherto been involved owing to Jane's fear that Cassie would be taken from her. The health visitor was concerned about Cassie's future and persuaded Jane to see a social worker to help consider some practical help in the home.

ISSUES FOR CONSIDERATION

- Overcoming Jane's fears that Cassie might be removed into "care" if social workers knew about her situation;
- Helping the HIV team to manage Jane's HIV treatment alongside her drug dependency through liaison with the GP;
- Facilitating referral to the children and families team and gaining Jane's trust so that present and future plans could be made;
- Providing home care to facilitate her living there and accessing medical care;
- Balancing care for Jane with concerns about Cassie through the stages of Jane's terminal illness and after her death.

STRUCTURE OF THE SESSION

Having a structure or "map" for the counselling session facilitates effective use of time for both clients and social worker and helps to integrate counselling into other tasks. This structure is equally applicable for use in a variety of other counselling situations. The following vignettes from an HIV case example will be used to demonstrate some of the steps.

1. **Think first or hypothesise** about the case prior to the session to help focus the initial contact based on knowledge about:

- Who made the referral;
- Age, sex, marital status;
- Cultural, ethnic, and social context;
- Stage of HIV infection;
- Other medical problems (drug use, hepatitis).

EXAMPLE:

Helen, a 28-year-old woman with a five-year-old child, is about to leave her husband. She has had HIV infection for three years which she acquired heterosexually outside her marriage. She attends a specialist HIV service and has been referred to the local authority social worker for help with rehousing.

The hypothesis could be that:

- Helen has HIV infection but is apparently well;
- She might have concerns about her past or future sexual relationships;
- The HIV status of her child is uncertain and might influence her decisions about the future;
- Differences between the doctor's perceptions about what the social worker could do about housing and what could be done in reality might create difficulties in relation to Helen's expectations of the social worker;
- Helen and her child can be regarded as a "one-parent family";
- There might be child-care issues for the immediate and long term future.

2. Decide whether to see the client **alone or with a colleague**. Joint interviewing (with health visitor, another social worker or a member of the hospital team) is an effective way of passing on skills, remaining neutral, and offering the client more than one perspective to the same problem.

EXAMPLE:
For the initial interview the social worker decided to meet Helen with the HIV community nurse specialist who knew her. The social worker wanted to focus on the expectations which had been raised about rehousing by the doctor and to learn more about her medical situation.

3. **Clarify the purpose** of the discussion (to give information, identify concerns, assess needs, and make an appropriate referral).

Social worker: *I am Jane the local authority social worker. I have been asked to see you by Dr Brown. Can you tell me what you understand about the reasons he had for wanting me to see you?*
Helen: *He said you would get me a flat (very tense looking).*

4. Note **reactions** and elicit main immediate concerns.

> ***Social worker:*** *Is that your main concern right now, or is there anything else you are worried about?*

5. **Identify concerns or wishes** and help people to be specific.

> ***Helen:*** *It is one of my problems, but not the only one. It's the HIV.*
> ***Social worker:*** *You say your main concern is the HIV. What is it about HIV that you are worried about?*
> ***Helen:*** *Both the certainty and uncertainty.*
> ***Social worker:*** *Explain to me a bit more about what are the certainties and uncertainties.*
> ***Helen:*** *Well, that I will die and that I don't know when.*

6. **Rank concerns** as this facilitates having small goals and helps to reduce anxiety to manageable proportions.

> ***Social worker:*** *Which is the greater concern right now, the certainty you perceive or the uncertainty? Where does your housing rank alongside all your other concerns?*
> ***Helen:*** *I suppose the certainty that I will die sooner than I had expected.*
> ***Social worker:*** *So with that in mind what is your main concern*
> ***Helen:*** *I suppose getting a flat as soon as possible.*

7. **Elicit and give information** about HIV and implications for future health or other relevant aspects.

> ***Social worker:*** *Explain to me what you understand about what treatments there are for HIV infection?*

8. Address who else might be involved with the client, including who else knows the client is seeking or requiring help.

> ***Social worker:*** *Who else knows about your problems and that you are meeting with us today?*
> ***Helen:*** *My mother. No one else and she is no help!*

9. Assess the medical, psychological, and social situation based on information gained from discussion and previous records.

EXAMPLE

The social worker learnt that Helen was quite well at present but was complaining of extreme fatigue. She was particularly agitated about leaving her husband and that she had no one else she could talk to. The social worker felt that Helen's expectations and those of the medical team might be unrealistic and that it could take some time for her to be rehoused. The social worker was concerned about Helen's daughter Sarah, whether she was infected with HIV or not, and what plans might be set in place for her in the future should her mother become ill. However, she did not want to raise too many issues at the first meeting.

10. Refer to others who might need to be involved in clients' care with their knowledge and permission (GP, health visitor, HIV-testing clinic).

> ***Social worker:*** *I would like to gain the support of your general practitioner and the health visitor. What are your views about this?*
> ***Helen:*** *I don't want them to know about the HIV. I never use my doctor.*
> ***Social worker:*** *I can see that you are afraid to tell anyone about the HIV, but how do you think it might be helpful to tell your GP?*
> ***Helen:*** *Well, I suppose if I was ill at home.*
> ***Social worker:*** *That is right. Also we will be able to get support from these people for your housing if you tell them everything about your circumstances.*

11. Record details of the interview, particularly the information given to the patient (discussion about HIV risk/testing and any other issues). Using a genogram (diagram depicting relationships with family and others) can help to rapidly build up a picture of the patient's social context (McGoldrick & Gerson, 1985).

> ***Social worker:*** *I am making some notes about what we have discussed, what needs to be done, and when we will meet again. I have also mapped out your family as we have been talking. Is this what it looks like?*
> ***Helen:*** *My father left my mother when I was three months old. I have never seen him.*

12. Summarise what has been observed and heard, **balancing reality** (fears of being infected/being infected) with **hope** (future care and support, or a long period of health).

> ***Social worker:*** *From what I have seen and heard today you are very stressed at the moment about a number of things – leaving your husband, having nowhere to go, and no one you can talk to. In addition, you have the responsibility for Sarah not knowing how long you have to live. Despite all this you are here today to try and better your situation. So somehow you have the strength to think about the things that are important to you now. I will do my best to help you get rehoused, but this may take some time. I would like you to make the application to the housing department yourself. I will ask Dr Brown to provide supporting medical information. I will come and see you at home in one week to review what is happening and see what else we might need to do to help with your housing.*

CONSULTATION AND SUPERVISION

The medical, social, and psychological issues associated with HIV can be complex. Having access to supervision and consultation can enhance the effectiveness of working with clients, their families, and the multidisciplinary team. HIV can evoke personal dilemmas related to lifestyle, morality, mortality, and views about birth and death for the social worker. Having opportunities to consider these issues in relation to work with clients can help maintain some neutrality, enhance effectiveness of the interventions, and reduce "burn out" when social workers have heavy case-loads.

Conclusion

If the aims and task of HIV counselling in the social work context are clear and defined, time can be used effectively for both worker and patient. Having a structure for sessions helps to raise issues and address them even if comprehensive information is not available. Counselling should be seen as an integral part of assessment, advocacy, information giving, and effective referral.

Interventions through the stages of HIV infection

INTRODUCTION

This chapter suggests possible social work interventions at different stages of HIV infection. Social workers, in common with other health care workers, can feel less informed about HIV than their clients. Many people with HIV are very well informed about new developments in the field through publications, the internet, and voluntary organisations working in their interests. This can result in workers feeling less confident about entering into discussion with these patients.

Many patients with HIV are now more willing to consider the latest HIV treatments of combination antiretroviral therapy which at the present time seem to prolong and improve quality of life. This is in marked contrast to the early 1990s. However, some patients remain diffident, afraid of side-effects and of "using up treatment options" before they are really unwell. Many people who believe that they are infected are coming forward for testing to access these new treatments which offer much more hope.

In the years before these new combination treatments were available there were more clearly demarcated stages of HIV infection. As more information has become available, it is now evident that there is no truly-symptom-free stage of HIV. Patients nowadays, would in most circumstances, be offered early antiretroviral treatment if it is indicated by a high rate of viral replication. This blurs the previous understanding of HIV infection. The patient has early HIV infection but is on treatment which should be viewed more as prophylaxis. Conceptually, however, it helps to differentiate between, for example, early infection from late stage disease. Prior to discussing stages of infection, we must first consider aspects of prevention and health promotion.

PREVENTION AND HEALTH PROMOTION

Social workers with their expertise and contact with disadvantaged, vulnerable individuals and groups have a vital role to play in the prevention of transmission. This means raising the issue of HIV whenever the opportunity presents itself.

Now, in the late-1990s, there is more certainty about what are and are not the risks of transmission. Some uncertainty still surrounds the risks associated with kissing and oral sex. However, in the absence of complete knowledge the information given, especially for young people, has to include a frankness about the lack of hard facts. This means being able to talk openly about sexual behaviour and helping clients assess the risks they may wish to take.

Prevention interventions rarely have an impact unless the client's knowledge, beliefs, and fears in relation to HIV are first elicited and particular risk factors are identified. HIV is most suitably included amongst the other health and social concerns (contraception, drug use, diet, smoking, other sexually transmitted diseases) raised in daily practice. Health promotion and prevention work can be done on an individual basis or through opportunities that might present themselves for group work, especially with adolescents.

CASE EXAMPLES

1. Adolescents

A group of adolescents in residential care are meeting with the social worker to discuss their concerns about being "in care", their relationships with social services and their parents. The social worker takes the opportunity to raise other important issues such as relationships with peers. She opens the discussion by asking each to say one thing that is important to people of their age. No one mentions sex. She expresses surprise and asks outright whether it is something that they ever think about. This leads into a discussion about taking care of their health, contraception, sexually transmitted diseases, and HIV. The subject has been broached and can lead onto finding out their concerns, knowledge, and beliefs about HIV and other sexually transmitted diseases.

2. Andrew: Is oral sex safe?

A 30-year-old man, Andrew, has been referred to a social worker for help in organising home care for his partner who is terminally ill. Andrew has never had an HIV test. He maintains that he and his partner have always practised "safe sex". For some time he has wanted to ask about the safety of oral sex, but never could summon the courage to do so in the hospital setting. He said to the social worker casually, *"What do you think about oral sex. Is it safe?"* It emerged that Andrew, although caring for his terminally ill partner, has another friend and is wanting to take the relationship further. The following excerpt is taken from their conversation about oral sex and focuses on prevention.

> ***Social worker:*** *Tell me what you know about the safety of oral sex or otherwise.*
> ***Andrew:*** *I've been told and have seen leaflets saying that it is safer than other sexual practices because there isn't much virus in saliva.*
> ***Social worker:*** *What about semen, if it is ingested?*
> ***Andrew:*** *That is what worries me.*
> ***Social worker:*** *Well, I cannot say for sure that oral sex is safe. It can be risky and it depends on the degree of risk people are prepared to take for themselves or others. If you decided to be safer what would you do?*
> ***Andrew:*** *Always use condoms I suppose.*
> ***Social worker:*** *Is there any difficulty about that?*
> ***Andrew:*** *Yes and no.*
> ***Social worker:*** *What are the difficulties?*
> ***Andrew:*** *Other people.*
> ***Social worker:*** *How would it affect your relationships with other people if you decided to be as safe as possible?*

HIV ANTIBODY TESTING AND DIAGNOSIS

Discussions about HIV infection inevitably lead to dilemmas about HIV testing. If social workers are to be encouraged to be more proactive in raising the issue of HIV, they need to examine their views in relation to HIV and be informed about HIV antibody testing. These factors can influence the approach taken when talking with clients, enhancing or deterring the way individuals consider their risks and whether or not they take up the option of testing.

There is no way of knowing if individuals are infected with HIV unless they have an antibody test. People may say that they have worries but may not reveal all their past risk activities. For all these reasons no complete reassurance can be given. Testing is the only way of ascertaining HIV status.

Testing and screening for HIV antibodies may also have a part to play in prevention of transmission. Those found to be infected can take steps to protect others (sexual activity, having children, breast feeding, sharing blood-bearing instruments). For women contemplating pregnancy or couples considering having unprotected sex, HIV screening is a way forward. HIV should now be amongst the battery of tests routinely *offered* for screening in antenatal care (Miller & Madge, 1997).

Social workers in local authority settings or voluntary organisations normally will not be involved in carrying out HIV testing themselves but will offer opportunities to discuss testing with their clients and prepare them in some measure for the outcome. Having an understanding of the issues involved in HIV testing can help social workers to do this more easily and confidently. The main issues surrounding HIV testing are:

- The client's views and perceptions of testing;
- The meaning of the antibody test;
- Its value for diagnosis;
- HIV treatment opportunities;
- Consequences for relationships.

A focused approach to the discussion about HIV testing enables the salient features to be covered in a limited time. Most difficulties can be addressed by social workers once the aims of the discussion are clear and referral sites for testing are identified.

The overall aims of pre-HIV antibody test discussion are

to provide information and to obtain "informed consent".
The content of this discussion varies from client to client
but can be kept brief and to the point, including:

- Raising the subject of HIV;
- Identifying knowledge about HIV transmission and methods of prevention;
- Exploring reasons for testing;
- Eliciting related medical history (other sexually transmitted diseases, travel, general health, drug use, blood transfusions);
- Identifying risk activities;
- Eliciting main benefits and any concerns about testing;
- Exploring possible reactions to positive and negative results;
- Considering relationships:
  Who else might be *affected*
  Who else *knows* about the concerns.
- Who else knows that the individual is considering testing;
- Who the client might *want* to tell (mother, partner);
- Who the client thinks *will* be told (friend);
- Who the client thinks *should* be told (partner, dentist, GP);
- Explaining where and how the test can be done;
- Using this opportunity to raise other matters (contraception, sexually transmitted diseases, and drug use) and to be specific about risk behaviours.

CASE 2 CONTINUED. Andrew: Is oral sex safe?
The social worker has already raised the subject of HIV
and clarified Andrew's knowledge about HIV transmission.

Social worker: *Have you any concerns for yourself about having HIV?*
Andrew: *Yes. I have never had a test but have always used condoms.*
Social worker: *Is testing something that you might now consider?*
Andrew: *Yes.*
Social worker: *What is it that makes you consider testing this time?*
Andrew: *Well, as I said, it is because I've got another relationship starting.*

Social worker: *Have you had any reason to be worried about your health? Or have you had any other sexually transmitted disease?*
Andrew: *No, it is only the oral sex.*
Social worker: *Just to help me, what do you understand about the risks from oral sex?*
Andrew: *Not much, except that it may not be 100% safe.*
Social worker: *Yes. That is correct. There is some risk associated with oral sex which we can discuss a little later. Tell me, Andrew, what do you know about the test?*
Andrew: *Oh, I know all about it and the "window period".*
Social worker: *So, just clarify for me your understanding about the "window period".*
Andrew: *If I am correct, if my test is negative I'm all right because my last risk was six months ago.*
Social worker: *That is correct. So what might be the main advantage to you in having the test?*
Andrew: *I've been worrying for a long time, and I'll know for sure as the last risk was six months ago.*
Social worker: *Who else knows about your worries about HIV?*
Andrew: *My partner.*
Social worker: *If the test showed you had HIV infection how do you think you would react?*
Andrew: *I have thought about that over and over, especially seeing my partner dying. I just don't know right now*
Social worker: *Although you don't know right now, what might be the first thing that would come into your mind?*
Andrew: *Who will look after me.*
Social worker: *Is there anyone you would tell or not want to tell?*
Andrew: *No one to begin with.*
Social worker: *To begin with, what is the main issue for you?*
Andrew: *Deciding whether or not to test.*

Social worker: *If you decide to have this test would you go to your GP or a testing clinic?*
Andrew: *Maybe a same-day-testing-and-result clinic. It has been a relief just to talk about it.*
Social worker: *Will talking be enough to help the worry or do you think testing finally will be more important?*
Andrew: *That's a good question. I had not thought about it like that. I need to have this test.*

THE CLINICALLY ASYMPTOMATIC STAGE OF HIV INFECTION

During the stage of HIV infection when there are few if any clinical symptoms, social workers are not likely to have much contact with the majority of patients who, in theory, should be able to continue their day-to-day living. However, some have pre-existing social and psychological problems and may initiate contact with health or social services following a diagnosis of HIV.

As there is no truly asymptomatic phase of HIV, this is a stage when treatment can be considered, even if patients appear well (due to high viral replication). Counselling can enhance patients' perceptions of these options by clarifying their wishes and beliefs relating to their treatment and care. Addressing issues of concern when patients are well can:

- Facilitate future care;
- Enhance treatment compliance;
- Optimise care management;
- Help them get on with their lives;
- Reduce the possibility of transmission to others.

Social workers' contact with patients during this stage will depend on individual circumstances. Some patients may refer themselves for practical help (advice about benefits, housing) and may also have concerns about more difficult issues (telling others, future illness, planning for the future care of children, giving up work, and telling families). An awareness of the practical, psychological, social, and cultural implications of HIV can help social workers respond most appropriately.

Recurring themes during this phase of HIV disease include:

- Vacillation between hope and hopelessness and belief and disbelief;
- Relationship issues (maintaining old ones, making new ones, practising 'safer' sex, keeping secrets, telling others);
- Dealing with the certainty (being infected) and the uncertainty (when, what symptoms will develop, long term effects of treatment);
- Coping with evolving and changing information about HIV (transmission, infections, and new treatment options);
- Deciding about having children, becoming pregnant and termination of pregnancy decisions, interventions during pregnancy and delivery, and breast feeding;
- Thoughts about living and dying, and coping with recurrent loss of peers;
- Disclosure (parents, family, friends, sexual partners, employers).

Understanding some of the issues for patients during this phase of HIV helps to clarify possible **tasks**.

- Re-enforcing the importance of regular monitoring and follow-up at specialist HIV centres for early detection and appropriate treatment. Coming to clinics is an unwelcome reminder of having HIV for some patients. For others regular contact helps them to feel more secure and provides additional support;
- Encouraging patients to obtain information about available medical treatments, drug trials, and new developments in care;
- Ensuring understanding about clinical and laboratory tests for monitoring (CD4 count, viral load) by checking:
  - What they know about tests;
  - What they want to know about results, and how they can best get this information;
  - How not knowing might impact on their care and relationship with the medical team;

Identifying and addressing beliefs (conventional medicine, alternative or complementary therapies, dying, living) which can facilitate patient management and enhanced compliance.

- Identifying and addressing main concerns at appropriate intervals;
- Addressing problems of discrimination and stigma by considering:
  - How they might start difficult conversations;
  - Dealing with reactions of others;
- Considering the "rights of the child" and those of parents (when parents do not want children to be tested, told the results of tests, or to allow treatment to be instigated);
- Preparing the patient for changes in health by appropriately eliciting:
  - Who they consider as their next-of-kin;
  - Future care and guardianship of children;
  - Who they would nominate to make decisions if they were unable to do so themselves;
  - Opinions about communicating information relevant to health and social carers (community nurse, GP, social workers).
- Encouraging liaison between GP, specialist care, and relevant carers.

Discussion about these issues should not be avoided for fear of raising clients' anxieties. They should be guided by indications from the patient of their concerns and should be balanced with interventions to maintain hope.

SYMPTOMATIC HIV DISEASE (ADVANCED HIV INFECTION), INCLUDING AIDS.

It is during the clinically symptomatic stage of HIV infection that social workers in local authority settings or voluntary organisations are most likely to have their first contact with patients owing to changes in an individual's health and social circumstances. Social workers may initially become involved through discharge planning from hospital.

The clinically symptomatic phase of illness brings:

- Increased hospital attendances and monitoring of immune function;
- Consideration of treatment options;
- Possible changes in the balance of relationships (from being a breadwinner to being cared for, being employed and independent to a position of dependency);
- Disfigurement and debilitation (loss of weight, sight, mobility)
- Increased emphasis on practical considerations (financial problems, making wills, care of children, increased physical and psychological dependency);
- Necessity or pressure to disclose the diagnosis (family, employers, friends) and prepare for the future;
- Whether they would prefer to be at home or in hospital if they became terminally ill;
- Views about life-sustaining measures (ventilation) and living wills.

Participation in therapeutic drug trials enables patients to have access to new treatments at an early stage before they are licensed. Most patients welcome this opportunity. For others, this increases their dilemmas about the efficacy of the drugs, the long term side-effects of such drugs, and whether they should be kept for "when they are really needed". Such decisions can be stressful for patients.

Assumptions should not be made about how patients will react when they become ill. For some it brings an end to a long period of uncertainty during which they have worried about when they will become ill. With the new combination drug therapies patients are able to have an improved quality – and, it seems, length – of life. This can bring about a different set of difficulties, especially in:

- Providing services, as the periods of well-being can be variable and unpredictable;
- Arranging and then ceasing services (home help, shopping, meals) can be difficult from both the service providers and recipient's points of view;
- Realistically costing service needs for the present and for the future. Services may have to be developed that are responsive to this fluctuating pattern of disability. Beds for in-patient care are currently less in demand, but such trends can change.

TERMINAL STAGE

Once patients have reached the terminal stage of illness and wish to die at home, social workers inevitably become involved with assessing needs, managing and reviewing care plans. They will, in some instances, become key workers liaising between hospital teams, GPs, community nurse specialists, and district nurses. In the terminal stage, friends and family often become more involved in decision making and may be part of the care team. In other cases, there may be tensions between the patient's wishes and those of close friends, partners, and family members.

The terminal phase holds special counselling challenges (conflicting wishes between patients and those close to them, maintaining hope whilst ceasing active treatment). Patients are managed more effectively if their concerns and those of people close to them are identified and addressed early.

Issues affecting the management of the patient and their close contacts in the terminal phase:

- The move from active treatment to palliative care is the main management issue affecting both medical and social care provision in this phase. Exploring and reviewing the patient's views about this at earlier stages of illness facilitate these decisions. For example,

  "If we were unable to cure your symptoms, how would you want us to help you?"

  "At this stage of your illness, your symptoms could be managed in hospital, a hospice, or at home: which would you prefer?"

- Maintaining hope is possible, even at this stage. For example,

  "You say that what you fear most is being alone and in pain. What do you know concerning the things that can be done for pain? Who would you like to be with you if you don't want to be alone?"

- Confidentiality and secrets (who knows about the diagnosis, how to respond to queries from friends and relatives).

  "If your mother or father asks about what is the matter with you, what do you want us to say?"

"What would you want your sister to tell your daughter about you if you were to die?"

- Legal and financial matters can become more urgent and may not be resolvable (making wills). The wish to obtain certain goals (travel to home of origin to die) may not be achievable. This is not uncommon with asylum seekers, students, or visitors who are ill whilst away from home,

  "If you are not able to travel home now what other wishes do you have that might be fulfilled?"

- Conflicts between the family of origin and of choice may come to the fore. The emphasis can shift from being patient-focused to the concerns of close contacts.
- Opportunities should be made for patients to discuss wishes and concerns about death and dying. However, assumptions should not be made that all patients want to "come to terms with death", or that it is necessary or possible to attend to "unfinished business" (see case example to follow).
- Nominating "next-of-kin" is important, especially for same-sex couples. Legally the next-of-kin is the nearest living relative unless specific legal arrangements have been made by naming another appointed person in a will.
- Consideration of post-mortem and death certificates with relatives is much harder if the patient's views are not known. Most often this matter is left for discussion with relatives after the patient's death, which makes it more difficult for all concerned. Patients and relatives may not want AIDS written on the death certificate. It is possible for doctors to avoid this by stating the cause of death as, for example, pneumonia, and indicating that further information can be given to the coroner or public health authority if required.
- Sometimes new health and social care workers become involved (palliative care physicians, nurses, family doctors, and social workers). There is a need to co-ordinate the care, the patient's wishes, and the concerns of the close contacts, as demonstrated in the following case example.

The needs of carers, partners (infected/uninfected), and orphans will begin to emerge.

CASE EXAMPLE

Patrick, aged 29, had always wanted to die at home. He had obtained council accommodation in London, away from his parents, with the help of a local authority social worker. After a brief time in a hospice he was able to return home with a full home-care package organised by the local authority social worker. He had also obtained the help of a "Buddy" (befriender) from a voluntary organisation to supplement this care. There had been many past difficulties for Patrick, apart from coming to terms with his HIV and the restrictions it imposed on his daily living. The greatest difficulties were in relation to his family. His mother was willing to help as much as possible, whilst his father was more distant and had not been well himself. Over time, a balance had been found between his need for their help and an equal determination on his part to retain independence and keep some distance between them. This meant that to respect his wishes his mother did not visit daily in his last days. The palliative care nurse, feeling that there was "unfinished business between them" wanted the social worker to arrange a joint meeting with the dying patient, herself, and his parents. The social worker was tempted to comply with this request of the nurse to meet the family. On reflection she considered that intervening at this late stage might give a message to the family that they could not manage alone. In addition the family had not made any special requests for help, and it seemed to be the wish of the nurse for a "good" death for Patrick with past difficulties resolved that was the motivation behind the suggestion. The social worker conveyed this view to the nurse in a sensitive way that helped the nurse to stand back and let the situation resolve itself.

This case demonstrates how different teams and professions can view situations in diverse ways. In this case the social worker's long-standing link with the family gave her the advantage and confidence to resist the request of the nurse, whilst at the same time recognising the need to keep discussion about Patrick open between the nurse and herself in the last days.

BEREAVEMENT

The death of the patient from HIV can be the beginning of new problems:

- Others might be infected, or fear that they are infected;
- The fear of social stigma might isolate the bereaved, who may be unable to disclose the cause of death to even close family, contacts, or neighbours;

- GPs, in particular, and social workers might also be caring for sexual partners and/or family, including children, of the deceased.

At appropriate times referral for specialist bereavement counselling might be indicated because:

- The bereaved are often left with no one to turn to;
- Some may be disinclined to return to the hospital where their relative or partner died;
- It might be the social worker (who arranged home care) who has the task of providing the initial bereavement counselling and arranging an appropriate referral.

CONCLUDING POINTS

Each stage of HIV brings different issues and challenges for patients to consider and for social workers to address. The changing profile of HIV testing, monitoring, and treatment has an impact on individuals at risk of and with HIV infection. In times of limited resources close attention needs to be paid to those most "at risk" in the population not only in terms of their needs, but for social workers to participate actively in the prevention of this infection. The changing epidemiology in the USA shows that those in lower income groups and other vulnerable populations are at higher risk of HIV. The same is true for Ireland and may become so for the UK. Social workers often have front line-links with these groups. In planning for the provision of social services, predicting need remains difficult with new and evolving treatments, enabling some individuals to have a longer span of good health than was previously expected.

A balance needs to be found between encouraging patients with HIV to attend for regular physical and psychological monitoring and creating dependence. HIV is a condition which can reduce choices and a sense of individual autonomy. The complexity and unpredictability of the disease progression does not always allow for permanent solutions to be provided.

Case examples: social work issues

INTRODUCTION

This chapter illustrates, through a variety of case examples, how the presence of HIV can complicate family and relationship situations, in particular those situations which are complex prior to the presence of HIV. In each case example, issues to consider for social work involvement are highlighted and approaches for dealing with them are suggested. Some special challenges from a practical and psychological point of view include:

- Implications at different stages of life and within the HIV progression;
- Discrimination and stigma;
- Bisexuality, homophobia, and secrets;
- Social, emotional, and cultural pressures to have children;
- Dealing with uncertainty;
- Drug users and chaotic family life;
- Care of children and child protection concerns.

CASE 1. JOE: TESTING DILEMMAS

PRESENTING PROBLEM

Joe, a Ugandan boy aged 18 months, has been admitted to the paediatric ward with enlarged lymph nodes on his neck. His mother, an asylum seeker from Uganda, is a single mother with an older daughter aged five years. The paediatrician suspects that Joe has HIV infection and asks the mother to consider an HIV test for him. The hospital social worker is asked to discuss HIV testing for Joe with the mother, and the implications of this. Such a scenario may cause anxiety for both the worker and mother, with both feeling overwhelmed.

GENOGRAM 1

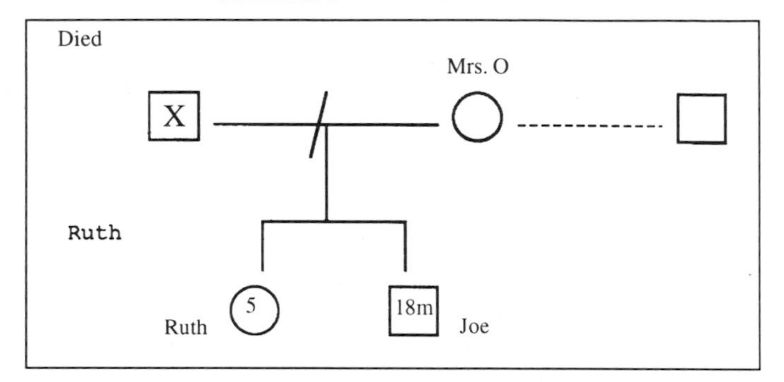

ISSUES TO CONSIDER

A) MEDICAL CONSIDERATIONS

- An accurate diagnosis cannot be made nor can appropriate medical treatment be instituted without laboratory evidence of infection through HIV antibody testing. Joe's condition may well deteriorate and opportunities for continued well-being will be missed. If the child is not infected other causes of his symptoms can be explored further;
- Testing a young child for HIV infection inevitably raises concerns about the mother's HIV status. Joe may be the first indication of HIV in the family and this might be a double blow for the mother;
- Uncertainty about how much the mother knows about HIV and fears of raising her anxiety;
- Does his mother already know that she is infected with HIV, or has she been worried about HIV?;
- Are her views based on her experience of HIV in Uganda?
- Which of the above (or maybe other concerns) is she most worried about?;
- Concerns may also be raised about the older daughter and her HIV status.

B) PRACTICAL CONCERNS

- The mother's residential status in the UK;
- Worries about her immigration situation and ability to remain in the UK together with fear of deportation may complicate her decisions about testing and being diagnosed as having HIV.

c) CONCERNS ABOUT THE MOTHER'S SOCIAL AND PSYCHOLOGICAL RESILIENCE

- Social workers may find it difficult to raise the issue of HIV with a mother of a sick child, fearing that she may become more anxious and distressed;
- Does she have a current partner, how would a diagnosis of HIV affect this relationship? What is his HIV status?;
- Being an asylum seeker from Uganda means that she may well have experienced trauma prior to fleeing Uganda;
- Has she had time to establish a home and some security for herself and her family in the UK?;
- Whether she has friends or extended family to support her in the UK, as she is a young single mother;
- She may have no contact with her family of origin and the father of her children.

ADDRESSING THE DILEMMAS

Some essentials in addressing the dilemmas include:

- Considering whether it would be best for this discussion to take place alone with the mother or in the presence of a member of the medical team;
- Maintaining calmness, taking time, and having patience;
- Eliciting the mother's main concerns at this point and not making assumptions about her worries,

  "Following our discussion so far, what is it that you are most concerned about at this point?";
- Developing a hypothesis about what may be issues for the mother and family at the point of referral;
- Using questions to establish knowledge, concerns, wishes and beliefs. Having a plan as to how to proceed based on the medical and social circumstances, especially the requirements of the medical team to have an antibody test result for Joe;
- Ensuring that the mother has accurate information, time to consider the options, and feels she has control over the choices as to how to proceed: for example,

  "Mrs O, Dr S has suggested testing Joe for HIV to help us find out what exactly is wrong with him. What are your views about this?"

"What do you know about how a child becomes infected with HIV?"
"Have you ever been concerned that you might have been at risk of HIV infection?"
"Have you ever been tested for HIV yourself?"
"You say that you are worried about whether you are infected. What do you know about HIV infection in adults?" '
"If Joe is tested for HIV and is positive, it is likely that you will also be infected. What do you know about the treatments available for HIV in the UK?"
"What do you see as the advantage of Joe being tested at the moment? What are your main fears?";

- Using hypothetical future-oriented questions to help the mother view difficulties from a different perspective.

"If Joe were to test HIV positive what might be your main concern?"
"You tell me that your mother is alive in Uganda and that you are very close to her. If she could hear our discussion today what would her advice to you be?"
"What do you think will happen if you decide not to have Joe tested?"
"How do you think the doctors will proceed if they are not able to make a firm diagnosis or rule out HIV?"
"You tell me that you have had to deal with some very difficult things in the past. What do you believe helped you keep going during that time?"
"What would help you to cope if the HIV test was to come back positive?"
"Is there anyone in this country with whom you could discuss these concerns and who might help you decide whether to have Joe tested or not?";

- Dealing with practical issues as an entrée to discussing more-complex personal problems.

"If the test did come back positive, the team here in the hospital could give you support and practical help, such as accessing better housing and legal advice regarding your immigration situation. Is there any other sort of assistance that you think might help make things a little easier for you and your family?"

OUTCOME

After some days and several interviews going over the same points raised above, Mrs O decided to have Joe tested. He was infected with HIV, treatment was instigated, he improved, and he went home. During his hospitalisation, Mrs O was assisted in applying for more appropriate housing and referred to a specialist agency for assistance with her immigration position. Just before Joe was discharged home from hospital she decided to have an HIV test for herself, but she did not return for some months to receive the result, which was positive. Nevertheless, she attended the paediatric clinic on a regular basis with Joe and could see the improvement in his health. Mrs O then attended a special women's HIV clinic for herself, and she remains well. She has not yet been able to face having her older child tested for HIV.

Mrs O has been rehoused and has received increased social security benefits owing to her and Joe's health situations. A referral to her local social services HIV team enabled access to a travel pass, phone installation, and some home care. The children's and families team helped her obtain a nursery place for Joe.

Over time she was able to make contact with a voluntary self-help organisation for women with HIV. The current people involved with the family's care at the present time are:

- The hospital HIV medical team (adult and paediatric);
- Hospital-based counsellor;
- General practitioner and health visitor;
- Social workers in the adult and children and family teams in social services.

CONCLUSIONS

Such a case could also present to a social worker in the community via the GP or health visitor if there were concerns about a child "failure to thrive" or symptoms of HIV infection. The social worker could work with the mother as described and then link her and the child into the local HIV treatment centre.

CASE 2. DISCRIMINATION AND STIGMA

PRESENTING PROBLEM

Mr Y is a 40-year-old professional man who has been in a relationship with Mr X for the past 10 years. Mr Y was worried that he had been exposed to HIV in the past, had not been feeling well for some months, and decided to have an HIV antibody test which proved to be positive. He subsequently told Mr X that he was HIV infected. Mr X decided to be tested and was found to be similarly infected.

Mr Y's elderly parents live outside London and he has a brother and sister with whom he is not very close. He decided not to tell his family of his diagnosis because he did not want to burden them unnecessarily. Nor did he tell any close friends because he was worried that news of his condition would affect his career.

His partner, Mr X, also decided not tell anyone about his diagnosis. Mr Y became progressively more unwell and in time had to work part time. He explained this by telling his employers and friends that he had a chronic chest condition. He was worried about how he would manage financially with reduced income.

GENOGRAM 2

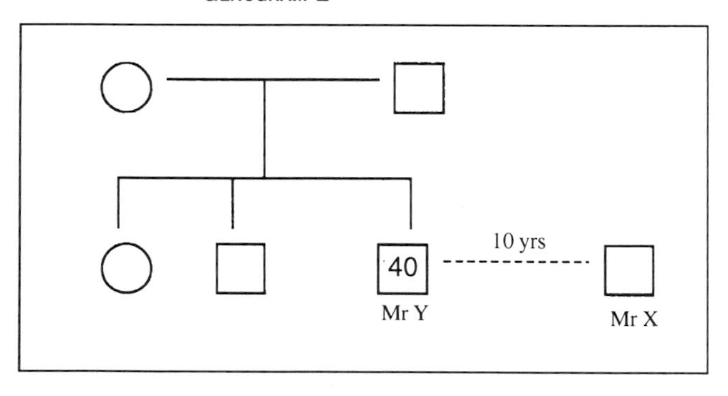

ISSUES TO ADDRESS

- Enabling Mr Y to obtain practical help;
- Developing a relationship over time so that more difficult issues can be addressed (telling friends, family, and employers about HIV, concerns about ceasing work, fears about poverty and death).

ADDRESSING THE ISSUES

- Focusing on practical needs and assisting access to services by alerting Mr Y to the entitlement to some DSS benefits owing to the deterioration in his health;
- Facilitating a local social services referral for a care needs assessment and to access other services (travel pass and taxicard);
- Discussing future concerns for himself and his partner Mr X (disabled person's parking disc in order to bring him to and from the hospital at a time when he might be too ill to travel on his own) and family;
- Using a genogram to highlight and clarify relationships;
- Addressing concerns about confidentiality by focusing on accessing practical services which could facilitate a less-threatening way forward.

OUTCOME

Mr Y's acceptance of practical help enabled the local authority social worker to tell him about other assistance that was available if he should need it in the future (home help and home care). Several months later Mr Y was admitted to hospital. On discharge he was able to link back with the social worker he had already met and home care was provided without delay. As his condition worsened, contact with his social worker increased and a comprehensive care package was set up.

CASE 3. BISEXUALITY: FAMILY SECRETS AND FEAR OF STIGMA

PRESENTING PROBLEM

Having advanced HIV disease, Mr B was referred through a private GP to a specialist HIV unit. He was a banker, married, with three children of eight months, five years, and eight years. His fears were that his wife might also be infected with HIV. His source of infection was a "relationship in New York". His wife was eventually tested and found to be infected. Neither he nor his wife wanted the baby HIV-antibody tested. Their main concerns were:

- Their relationship;
- Fears about friends and work contacts learning of the wife's infection;
- Finding a way to manage Mr B's declining health.

GENOGRAM 3

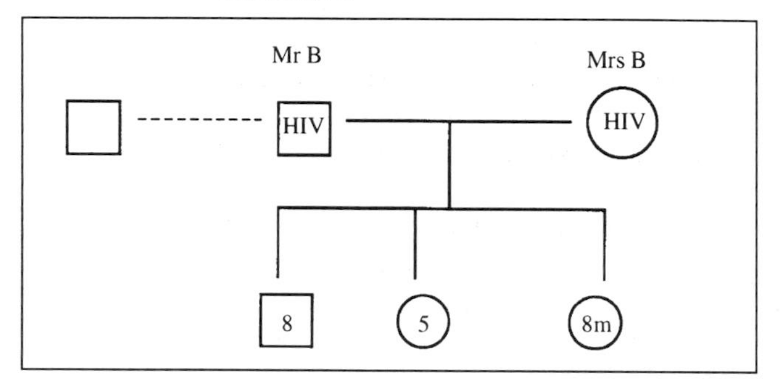

ISSUES TO ADDRESS

- Developing a sufficiently good relationship with Mr B and then his wife so that their concerns (marital relationship, fears of discrimination for wife and children, future of the children) and those of the hospital team (wife's health and HIV situation of the youngest child) could be addressed;
- Assessing with the couple their practical and emotional needs and deciding on "appropriate" actions;
- Maintaining a relationship with wife after the patient's death to enable her to access appropriate care and treatment when she felt ready to do so;
- Considering the changes in treatment options over the years.

ADDRESSING THE ISSUES

- Adopting a neutral, yet empathic, approach to enable issues to be raised and discussed;
- Offering practical help as an entrée to discussing more sensitive issues (relationships, children's future);
- Dealing with issues slowly, step by step, and at the couples and individual's pace, despite the medical concerns about the child's health.

CONCLUSIONS

After some months of attending the specialist centre, close family members were eventually told of the HIV problem because future plans had to be considered for the three children. The wife found it very difficult to manage from an emotional and practical point of view. With time she agreed that the local social services and nursing agency be approached to provide some home care, even though finances were not an issue. Mr B died some years later. The wife Mrs. B avoided contact for several years after that, never having attended for her own health, choosing to ignore the problem. A new relationship precipitated renewed contact with Mrs B.

Initially, fears about death, dying, illness and confidentiality prevented this couple from accessing adequate psychosocial and practical help. Sometimes responding to needs in times of crisis is the only starting point.

CASE 4. PREGNANCY AND SECRETS

PRESENTING PROBLEM

Miss S is a 24-year-old single woman who had come to the UK as a student from Kurdistan and now had residency qualification in the UK. She became infected with HIV whilst in a relationship with a man who had AIDS and who had not told her that he was infected. This man subsequently died. She then entered a relationship with a man from her own ethnic background whom she was unable to tell about her HIV infection condition. This relationship was important in providing some stability in her life. The couple used condoms only intermittently because the boy-friend was not keen on using them. She was well from an HIV perspective and was keen to have children at some point. From time to time she came to the clinic requesting a pregnancy test, and on one occasion the test proved to be positive. She then had to consider whether to proceed with the pregnancy or not.

GENOGRAM 4

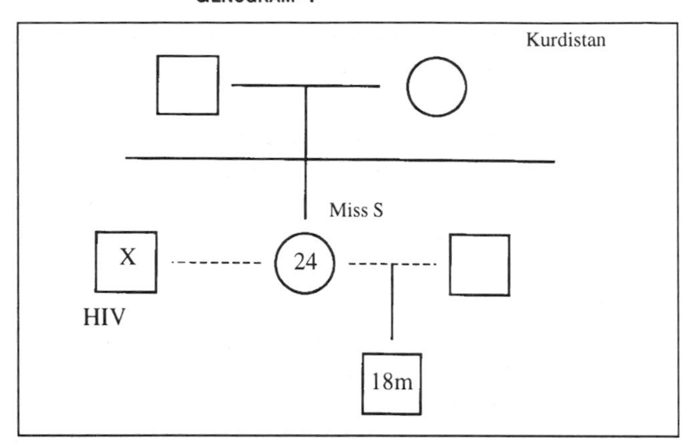

ISSUES TO ADDRESS

- Conflicts between preserving confidentiality for Miss S and "public health" issues of her partner being uninformed of her HIV infection;
- Helping Miss S understand and weigh up the risks of the baby being infected with HIV if she proceeded with the pregnancy;
- Explaining the treatment options available to reduce the risk of the baby being infected;
- Helping her think about how she would cope if the baby was infected;
- How she would cope as a single mother with a young baby;
- Helping her reach a decision about the pregnancy within a short space of time.

ADDRESSING THE ISSUES

- Using hypothetical future-oriented questions helped Miss S address various difficult issues,

  "What might be your main concerns if you continued with the pregnancy or if you decide to have a termination?";
- Identifying and addressing practical and emotional issues within a short time frame.

  "What do you understand about the risks of transmission to your partner and baby?"

> *"If you became unwell, or even died, who might help care for the baby?"*
> *"How might you manage if your baby was infected and became ill or died?"*
> *"As it will be uncertain for about 18 months whether or not your baby will be infected, how will you manage during this time?"*;

- Ranking concerns and dealing with one issue at a time, for example,

  > *"Which is the main concern for you: telling your partner, deciding about the pregnancy, or something else?"*;

- Continuing to address the importance of informing her sexual partner, initially encouraging her to do so herself, and then by applying other tactics through questions.

  > *"It is a difficulty for me knowing that your partner is unaware of your HIV and that he too may be infected without knowing. What is your main concern in telling him?"*
  > *"If you did tell him, how do you think he would respond?"*
  > *"How might this affect your relationship?"*
  > *"If he did leave you, how do you think you would cope?"*
  > *"You are now receiving treatment for your HIV. If your partner is infected and doesn't know, what do you think about how his health might be affected?"*
  > *"Do you think it would be easier to tell him now while you are well or when he finds out later if you became ill?"*;

- Linking her with an obstetrician and gynaecologist so that she could discuss her options with them.

OUTCOME

Miss S decided to continue with the pregnancy and to take antiretroviral treatment during the pregnancy and labour in order to reduce the risks of transmitting HIV to her baby. She had a baby boy who was not infected with HIV. She still has not told her partner that she has HIV. This remains a problem which all the health care and social care professionals have to continue to address. Fears of her discontinuing with medical care for herself have to date deterred the medical team from more forcefully addressing the need to tell her partner. She has linked back with her family in Kurdistan and has arranged for them to care for her baby in the event of her death, but this still leaves in doubt the putative father's views about the child's future.

CONCLUSIONS.

This is a situation that highlights the rights of the individual versus "public health". The health care workers did not want to push the mother away from obtaining the care she needed for herself and her child.

CASE 5. MENTAL HEALTH PROBLEMS

PRESENTING PROBLEM

Mr P is a 25-year-old single gay man who came to have an HIV test because he felt that he had been at risk. He was found to be infected with HIV. He had been brought up in care and had little or no contact with his family. He had long-standing personality difficulties, and these were exacerbated by a diagnosis of HIV infection. He tended to present both to his treating centre and to other hospitals in crisis, either requesting emergency financial assistance or after having taken an overdose. It transpired that he was attending two HIV treatment centres for HIV care. He had damaged his flat and had been rehoused in temporary accommodation in another borough. There was a threat of court action over the damage to his flat.

GENOGRAM 5

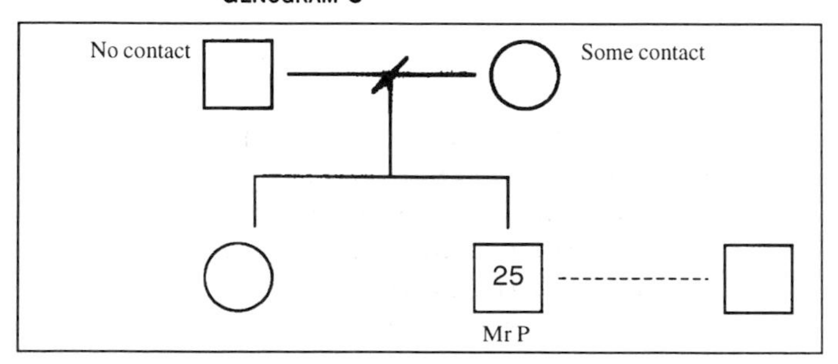

ISSUES TO ADDRESS

- Clarifying his support network of all involved in his health and social care;
- Eliciting his main difficulties and what he would consider to be most helpful at the present time;
- Assessing, as far as possible, how this man's past life events had precipitated his recent erratic behaviour and which were now due to or exacerbated by HIV;
- Considering how best to provide him with some stability and continuity of care from a practical and emotional point of view;
- Ascertaining his mental state to determine if psychiatric treatment was indicated;
- Attempting to pre-empt Mr P presenting in crisis with neither sufficient time nor the appropriate staff to deal adequately with the situation.

ADDRESSING THE ISSUES

- Nominating a key worker to co-ordinate assessment, current treatment, and future care;
- Using the pre-existing relationship in one HIV centre (who helped him sort out practical issues, housing benefits) to be the co-ordinator;
- Assessing what had precipitated his current difficulties;
- Facilitating a psychiatric assessment;
- Liaising with the other HIV treatment centre that he had also been attending to ascertain their views;
- Arranging a case conference with all those involved to formulate a plan to try to reduce future crises.

OUTCOME

At the case conference it was decided to try to focus his HIV care in the nearest treatment centre. An attempt was made to enable him to have regular psychiatric follow-up as well as a local authority social worker who would help him with practical difficulties. Clarification of how much his past difficulties and HIV contributed to his mental and emotional instability remained difficult to ascertain. He was started on an antiretroviral drug (AZT) which is known to cross the blood-brain barrier. An HIV diagnosis was important to allow this to happen.

CONCLUSIONS

The main difficulty in this case was the co-ordination of all those involved. The way Mr P split his health and social care mirrored his chaotic lifestyle and increased the chances of him presenting in a crisis. Open access for HIV medical care increases chances of different sources being involved.

CASE 6. PLANNING CARE FOR CHILDREN

PRESENTING PROBLEM

Mrs N is a 40-year-old Ugandan woman who has four children, aged 16, 14, and 10 years from an earlier marriage, and a 4-year-old child from a more recent union. The second relationship broke down when her husband discovered that she had AIDS when she was admitted to hospital very unwell. Mrs N was diagnosed as having HIV six years ago when she had an HIV test following a miscarriage. She had consistently refused to tell her husband that she had HIV, fearing that he would leave her. Two years after her diagnosis she had the baby who is now 4 years old and who is HIV negative. Because Mrs N was very unwell, the staff in the treatment centre were very concerned about care of her children in the event of her death. Mrs N had always been very concerned about confidentiality and would never consider a referral to any other agency for help.

GENOGRAM 6

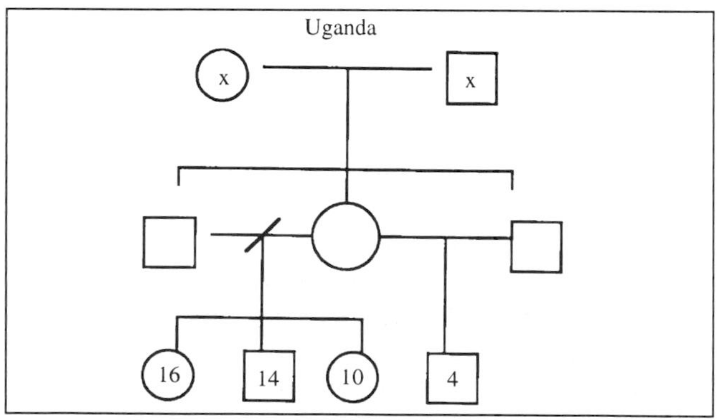

ISSUES TO ADDRESS

- Dealing with Mrs N's fears of disclosure and confidentiality whilst recognising the range of practical and emotional issues that might lead to involvement of others;
- Ascertaining what her children knew about her health and her prognosis;
- Assessing how she would manage on discharge from hospital because she was very weak and would be unable to care for herself and her children on her own includes exploring:
  - what sort of help would she be willing to accept;
  - who might be able to provide this help;
  - who else was around who might be able to help her.
- Eliciting her views about care for her children if she became too ill to care for them or if she died;
- Addressing the possible impact on her children if she did not make any arrangements for their future.

ADDRESSING THE ISSUES

Using the long-standing relationships Mrs N had with staff in the treatment centre to raise difficult issues by:

- Giving prominence to the cultural constraints in order to understand Mrs N's perspective;
- Liaising with the HIV community nurse specialist to monitor her medication at home as an entrée to linking her with her local social services department (arranging for the children and families team to provide an escort for the youngest child to and from school);
- Addressing the practical issue of home care as a first step in beginning to consider the more sensitive problems (needs of the children).

OUTCOME

Mrs N went home. Through the provision of practical help she became well linked with the adult and disability team of the local social services department (home care) and with the children and families team (care for the children). Mrs N died in a short space of time. The father took care of her youngest child, and the older children are in the care of a cousin of Mrs N, who is their guardian. The children's care is being monitored by the children and families team as the arrangements had of necessity to be made in haste and without due consideration because of Mrs N's rapidly deteriorating health. Bereavement issues for those "orphaned" children are of concern to the social worker.

CASE 7. DRUGS USE, PREGNANCY, AND CHILD PROTECTION ISSUES

PRESENTING PROBLEM

Giovanni and Mary are two drug-users who are HIV infected. Giovanni is a young, single, Italian man who has been living in the UK for several years. He was diagnosed with HIV some years ago and he is currently on a methadone maintenance programme. Mary is a young English woman who is also HIV+ and is on a methadone programme. She is single but has had two children who do not live with her. Her two older children are cared for by their respective fathers. She has week-end contact with the second child. Giovanni and Mary met whilst they were staying in a respite centre after they had taken an overdose. After a couple of months Mary discovered she was pregnant, and was undecided as to whether she wanted to continue with the pregnancy. Giovanni was very keen that she should go ahead and have their baby. Their relationship from the outset was a stormy one. Giovanni describes himself as a "volatile" man and attributes this to his Italian temperament.

Mary and Giovanni had separate counsellors at the HIV treatment centre. Early on, Mary disclosed to her counsellor that there was some domestic violence in her relationship with Giovanni, but she was not prepared for this to be discussed with Giovanni in a joint session.

When Mary's pregnancy was confirmed, she was introduced to the HIV specialist midwife and obstetrician to discuss the pregnancy and antenatal care. The parents were subsequently introduced to the paediatrician who would be caring for the baby. It was difficult for the professionals to co-ordinate their care because there were so many people involved with the case, and each had a slightly different perspective on how they were managing.

ISSUES TO ADDRESS

- Concerns about the safety of the child:
  - Past and current child protection issues;
  - Extent of domestic violence;
  - The couple's ability to parent the expected infant.
- Drugs-using issues:
  - Whether previous clinic appointments were regular;
  - Methadone use and whether there are other drugs.
- Issues related to the baby:
  - How will they cope with the baby going into a special care baby unit for methadone withdrawal;
  - Suitability of their living arrangements for coping with a young infant.
- Key worker issues were about who would be the most suitable professionals for the many issues:
  - Drugs services included counsellors for each and a doctor scripting the methadone;
  - HIV services included doctors, HIV counsellors for each, specialist HIV midwife, obstetrician, and paediatrician;
  - Social services included adult and disability team social workers from their respective social services departments in different boroughs;
  - Respite centre for day care included support workers for each and day care staff.

ADDRESSING THE ISSUES

- Clarify who is the most appropriate person to raise the concerns with the parents;
- Elicit and clarify their main concerns (coping with their baby in a special care baby unit, obtaining a larger flat);
- Develop an understanding of both Mary and Giovanni by obtaining a history, and engaging them over those issues of main concern;
- Rank main concerns from the patients' point of view and the social worker's perspective;
- Organise a planning meeting to:
  - Obtain the different professionals' perspectives and involvement with the family;
  - Identify any concerns especially about the couple's ability to parent or whether the child might be at risk;
  - Appoint a key worker.

- Raising concerns prior to the birth of the baby to:
  - Allow the parents some time to prepare for what will happen after the birth;
  - Understand the extent of support available to help them care for their baby;
  - Clarify concerns of both professionals and Mary and Giovanni (as a couple, individually) for the baby.

OUTCOME

During the pregnancy Mary made a concentrated effort to reduce the amount of methadone she was receiving for her addiction because of her concern for her unborn child. The pregnancy was at times stormy with both Mary and Giovanni seeing a variety of professionals at different times. The HIV specialist midwife made the referral to the children and families team three weeks before the baby was due to be born. A case conference was held to discuss whether the baby needed to be put on the "at risk" register at birth. Twelve professionals involved with the family attended the case conference and all concerns were addressed. The couple were very angry when the issue of domestic violence was mentioned and accused staff of breaking confidence. A decision was made not to place the baby on the "at risk" register at birth, as he or she would be in the special care baby unit for up to a month following birth for methadone withdrawal. It was agreed that a pre-discharge planning meeting would be held prior to the baby's discharge home. The baby was born via Caesarean section to reduce the risks of HIV transmission.

CONCLUSIONS

This case demonstrates the complex issues that might have to be addressed when HIV is added to pre-existing drug problems and psychological frailty. All these are made more complex when dealing with the best interests of the child as well as those of the index patient/s. In such cases the decisions have to be taken by individual professionals in specialist fields, and often the local authority social worker acts as co-ordinator.

Epilogue

The future role of social work in the field of HIV will continue to depend largely on the willingness, interest, and expertise of individual social workers. From a service-provision perspective it is likely to be "mainstreamed" with specialist posts under threat. Dedicated finance may well in the future continue to decline. The social service model of HIV care may follow that of the health service. The Department of Health is now rethinking directing funding to centres of expertise where large teams keep abreast of monitoring tests and new treatments. Where funding is placed and ultimately where social work fits in depends to a large extent on the impact of treatments on the natural history of HIV infection. The HIV epidemic still points to large, urban areas as the places where specialised services will be consolidated. Local London boroughs as well as other centres in the country where HIV has tended to be concentrated will serve the largest number of cases. Elsewhere in the country generic teams are likely to serve a much smaller number. HIV diagnosis has to be readily integrated into mainstream medical care (general practice, family planning, and hospitals). From a social services perspective people are living longer, and support may be needed in different ways.

We are currently at an exciting phase in the epidemic with seemingly-more-effective treatments available. However, these new treatments pose different problems and dilemmas for patients and health care staff. These include when to start treatment, what combination of drugs to use, and the difficulty for patients in adhering to complicated regimens. Dilemmas about treatments for HIV infection will dominate the scene in the foreseeable future. It is not yet clear what the long term side-effects will be and for how long these treatments will be effective. Issues about transmission of the virus will continue to focus on helping people to have the right information and motivation to keep behaviour safe. To do this over a longer time-span may become more rather than less of a problem, especially if patients feel well.

From a social work perspective it is not clear what sort of help patients will need whilst on these new treatments. Some will need help because of the side-effects, some will be in better health but will not be well enough to work or be totally independent. Many may have fluctuations in their health.

If social workers have the vision there is an area of need to be met. The current drug regimens are expensive and there are issues about compliance that are emerging which have cost implications and also could affect the course of illness and prognosis for patients. Closer links with treatment centres and general practitioners could help to tackle this problem.

As more families are found to have members infected there will be an increase in the demand for care for both children and parents infected and affected. In the future, as more women choose to have children, different problems will emerge. Social workers may also see a role for themselves in addressing some of the issues that might arise for these women and for those who may be unaware of their HIV situation. In the pre-conception and antenatal phases little more is needed than the opening up of discussion about HIV with the wide range of women with whom social workers come into contact.

As more people from ethnic minorities are found to be infected, social workers will have to face the challenges of discussing sensitive issues and dealing with the practical implications of different cultures and beliefs.

Whilst social workers have long experience in working with individuals and families affected by chronic illness, the impact of HIV has particular challenges which need flexible, creative approaches and packages of care. It currently varies from local authority to local authority as to how much the broad spectrum of HIV issues are seen as "within the social work remit" currently variable. HIV prevention work needs to continue, and this is an area where social workers, wherever they work and whatever they do, hold a key role, particularly with vulnerable people. A unique aspect of HIV infection is that it can affect professionals and their clients alike as it results from human frailties and sexual behaviour that are part of daily living for most.

We, the authors, have worked in the field of HIV since the mid-1980s in a variety of settings and in a number of countries, the UK and Ireland. We have had experience in collaborating with many different colleagues from different professional backgrounds. We have found that the needs of individuals and families range from simple and practical (travel difficulties) to the most complex (managing seemingly intractable problems). Our view is that the training, experience, and qualities of social workers are ideally suited to addressing this range of needs. This combination of factors secured our commitment to writing this book. We hope that social worker colleagues will find some of the ideas of value not only in their approach to HIV but also for other problems which they may face. Working in the field of HIV has broadened and enhanced our views and perspectives, and we have found these ideas and approaches useful in other situations.

Titles available in the Practitioner's Guide series

Family Support *Ruth Gardner*

Family support has attracted much less attention in terms of research and development than the more clearly defined systems for children in need of statutory protection and/or those looked after by local authorities. Yet it is a legal requirement of the Children Act (England and Wales) 1989, backed up by the UN Convention on the Rights of the Child. This book describes the essential elements of good family support and gives examples of research, planning, budget management and evaluated practice. It is essential reading for managers and practitioners, commissioning or providing these services, in all settings.

ISBN: 1 86178 026 5

Confronting Disabling Barriers: towards making organisations accessible
John Swain, Maureen Gillman & Sally French

Little has been written for social workers and other professionals on disabling barriers within institutions. This guide draws upon the discipline of disability studies to assist practitioners who seek to make their organisations accessible to disabled people. This guide analyses institutional discrimination against disabled people and highlights ways in which organisations can become more acessible to them. The authors use a civil rights perspective underpinned by the social model of disability.

ISBN: 1 86178 027 3

The Work of the Guardian ad Litem *Anna Kerr & Eva Gregory*

The 1989 Children Act, as applied to England and Wales, and its subsequent developments have created a new role for the guardian ad litem. Their task has become more complex, responsible, absorbing and continuously changing. This book provides an informative and practical approach to the work involved. Apart from acting as a basic guidebook for practising guardians, it should appeal to social work consultants, solicitors, and others working in the child care field.

ISBN: 1 86178 024 9

Poverty *Monica Dowling*

This ethnographic study of two social work teams combines a participant observation study of social workers with an analysis of the relationship between poverty and social work. It also incorporates findings from a three year qualitative study of social service users' and carers' experiences of community care. The book develops an unusual eclectic approach by applying psychological, sociological, and social policy constructs to the study of poverty and social work. In conclusion it points the way forward for future social work practice, policy and reserarch in relation to issues of financial deprivation and social exclusion.

ISBN: 1 86178 025 7

Appendix

ABBREVIATIONS

AIDS: Acquired Immune Deficiency Syndrome
AZT: Zidovudine
CDC: Centres for Disease Control, Atlanta
DOH: Department of Health
DSS: Department of Social Security
GP: General practitioner
GUM: Genito-urinary medicine
HIV: Human Immunodeficiency virus
IVDU: Intravenous drug user
KS: Kaposi's sarcoma
PCP: Pneumocystis Carinii pneumonia
STD: Sexually transmitted disease
UK: United Kingdom
USA: United States of America

References

Adler M W. Sexual health – a Health of the Nation failure. *BMJ.* 1997;314: 1743-7.

BHIVA Guidelines Co-ordinating Committee. British HIV Association guidelines for antiretroviral treatment of HIV seropositive individuals. *Lancet* 1997; 349: 1086-92.

Bor R, Miller R, Goldman E. HIV/AIDS and the family: a review of research in the first decade. *Journal of Family Therapy* 1993; 15: 187-205.

Bor R, Miller R, Perry L. AIDS counselling: setting up a new service in a district teaching hospital. *Hospital and Health Services Review* 1987; Sept:221-3.

Carballo M, Miller D. HIV counselling: problems and opportunities in defining the new agenda for the 1990s. *AIDS Care* 1989; 1: 117-23.

Cecchin G. Hypothesising, circularity, and neutrality revisited: an invitation to curiosity. *Family Process* 1987; 26: 405-13.

Department of Health. *Guidelines for pre-test discussion on HIV testing*. PL/CMO/(96)1 London: HMSO, 1996.

Gaitley R, Mallinson W, Taylor D. *HIV-AIDS, A Social Work Perspective*. Birmingham: Venture Press, 1993.

Johnstone F. D. HIV and pregnancy. *British Journal of Obstetrics and Gynaecology* 1996; 103: 1184-1190.

Kitahata M., Koepsell T. D., Deyo R. A., Maxwell C. L., Dodge W. T., Wagner E. H. Physician's experience with the acquired immunodeficiency syndrome as a factor in patients' survival. *New England Journal of Medicine* 1996; 334: 11; 701-6.

Maguire P., Faulkner A. Communicate with cancer patients: 2. Handling uncertainty, collusion, and denial. *BMJ* 1988; 297: 972-4.

McGoldrick M., Gerson R. *Genograms in Family Assessment.* New York: W. W. Norton, 1985.

Middleton L. *The Art of Assessment. Practitioner's Guide.* Venture Press 1997.

Miller D, Weber J, Green J, editors. *The management of AIDS patients*. Basingstoke: The Macmillan Press, 1986.

Miller R, Bor R. *AIDS: a guide to clinical counselling.* London: Science Press, 1988.

Miller R., Goldman E., Bor R., Kernoff P. AIDS and children: some of the issues in haemophilia care and how to address them. *AIDS Care* 1989; 1: 59-65.

Miller R., Madge S. The place of counselling in the prevention, diagnosis and management of HIV infection'. In: Mindel A., Miller R., editors. *AIDS: a pocket book of diagnosis and management*. 1990. 2nd ed. London: Arnold, 1996: 266-80.

Miller R., Madge S. Routine HIV testing in antenatal care: time to move on. *The Diplomate 1997;* 4:26-31

Mounteney Jane and Shapiro Harry. *Drugs, Children and Families. Practitioner's Guide*, Birmingham: Venture Press 1998.

Scarlatti G. Paediatric HIV infection. *Lancet* 1996; 348: 863-8.

Singh S., and Madge, S. *Caring for people with HIV. A community perspective.* Hampshire: Ashgate Publishing Ltd, 1998.

Squire S. B., Elford J., Bor R., Tilsed G., Salt H., Bagdades E. K., et al. Open access clinic providing HIV-1 antibody results on day of testing: the first twelve months. *BMJ* 1991. 302: 1383-6

Unlinked Anonymous Surveys Steering Group. *Unlinked anonymous HIV prevalence monitoring programme in England and Wales*. 1996. 35-40.

Dealing with Aggression *Brian Littlechild*

How can aggression and violence to staff in social work and social care settings be managed? This book sets out an integrated approach to the wide range of problems presented by aggression and violence. It covers risk assessment and coping strategies from perspectives of the different individuals, staff groups and agencies involved. The best strategies for dealing with aggression face-to-face are presented, as are ways risk can be most effectively reduced. For students and experienced workers alike, this book gives a comprehensive account of how to increase safety at work.

ISBN: 1 873878 98 2

Down's Syndrome and Dementia *Diana Kerr*

This book defines good practice in needs assessment and the provision of services for the growing number of people with Down's Syndrome and Dementia. It is based on a social model which demands that we see the person first and the disease second. It suggests ways of maintaining choice and the best quality of life for people whose control is diminishing. It gives many practical examples of ways in which workers and carers can intervene to support people and avoid behaviour and practices which disempower and can harm.

ISBN: 1 86178 017 6

Drugs, Children and Families *Jane Mounteney & Harry Shapiro*

This book aims to demystify the drug phenomenon, and increase social workers' knowledge of drug use, by providing a range of up-to-date information about drugs and their effects, by exploring ways drug use may arise as an issue for clients and social services departments and through exploration of a range of social work interventions. It draws on relevant research and highlights concerns in relation to interventions and provision for young people with drug use problems.

ISBN: 1 86178 013 3

Working with Visually Impaired People: Bridging Theory and Practice
Sally French, Maureen Gillman & John Swain

This guide has been written from the experience of visually disabled people and the growing voice of the Disabled People's Movement. The authors, two of whom are visually disabled, take a civil rights perspective to visual disability, which is underpinned by the social model of disability. The book draws on the discipline of disability studies to guide practitioners who seek to assist visually disabled people to fulfil the lifestyles of their choice.

ISBN: 1 86178 014 0

Challenging Local Authority Decisions *Ann McDonald*

This book examines how dissatisfaction with outcomes can be used positively to challenge local authority decisions. Sometimes it will be the service provision that is challenged; other times, it will be how the decision is reached and the procedures used which are considered oppressive or unfair. All practitioners should know how to challenge local authority decisions through use of complaints procedures; default powers; referrals to the Ombudsman or through the courts. In doing so good practice is reinforced, legality is tested and rights upheld.

ISBN: 1 86178 015 X

Deafness and the Hearing *Jennifer Harris*

This book invites a radical change in the majority view on Deafness. The author spent four years studying an organisation of Deaf people in the UK and analysing the reactions of the Hearing majority. The results were dramatic; descriptions of stigmatism, oppressive practice and prejudicial attitudes emerged. The message of the book is that it is not deafness itself which determines social exclusion but entrenched prejudicial attitudes of 'the Hearing'.

ISBN: 1 86178 016 8

The Art of Assessment *Laura Middleton*

Good assessment is fundamental to good practice; for all potential service users regardless of age. It is an analytical process that requires intelligence, logic, flexibility, open-mindedness and creativity, and it should be experienced by the consumer as a positive contribution to their life. But it is more complicated than that. No assessment occurs in isolation, but within a competitive and often hostile environment which has to be understood and managed. This book offers a rough guide to this changing and imperfect world, and suggests a model for a value-based assessment within it.

ISBN: 1 873878 87 7

Community Care: Working in Partnership with Service Users
Jenny Morris

This book sets out four principles for working in partnership with people who need support in their daily lives: entitlement; the social model for disability; needs-led assessment; and promoting choice and control. Drawing on the wealth of research and information now available about how to work in ways which empower people. Examples are given relating to all the community care service user groups – older people, people with learning difficulties, those with physical/sensory impairment and people who use mental health services.

ISBN: 1 873878 91 5

Dilemmas of Financial Assessment *Greta Bradley & Jill Manthorpe*

The implementation of the NHS and Community Care Act 1990 has impacted on the lives of service users and social workers. This book explores one important area of change: the increasing emphasis on assessing users' financial circumstances in order to maximise their incomes but also to establish their ability to pay for services. For many social workers this is new ground. Some experienced social workers feel anxious and torn between the new culture of community care and the values they associate with traditional social work tasks.

ISBN: 1 873878 90 7